Kaizen
Event Implementation
Manual

Kaizen Event Implementation Manual

Geoffrey Mika

Society of Manufacturing Engineers
Dearborn, Michigan

Library of Congress Catalog Card Number: 2006928139

International Standard Book Number: 0-87263-849-9

Additional copies may be obtained by contacting:
Society of Manufacturing Engineers
Customer Service
One SME Drive, P.O. Box 930
Dearborn, Michigan 48121
1-800-733-4763
www.sme.org

SME staff who participated in producing this book:
Rosemary Csizmadia, Production Editor
Steve Bollinger, Manager, Book & Video Pubications
Frank Bania, Cover Design
Frances Kania, Administrative Coordinator

Printed in the United States of America

Table of Contents

Preface

KAIZEN IS A BEGINNING

Kaizen is a tool, originally used by Toyota, to foster continuous improvement within its production system. It is now used around the world by many companies who have adapted it to suit their individual needs and customs.

The main goal of the *Kaizen Implementation Manual* is to bring a level of competence and understanding to kaizen event participants so they may be self-sufficient in the application and use of kaizen. Now in its fifth edition, this manual has seen use in many industries for wide-ranging applications. It is designed to help you understand, organize, plan, and implement your own kaizen event in any setting.

THE LEAN JOURNEY

The lean journey down the road to improvement is sometimes bumpy. Other times, it is a super-highway. It is a road that never ends. The journey is never dull or unchallenging. It is exciting, enlightening, and most of all, fun! Kaizen presents a chance to do things in ways that are new to many people. And, it is a chance for everyone to contribute, be recognized, and excel.

In the past, one complaint heard universally throughout companies was, "No one ever listens to me when I try to tell them how to fix something." Or, "Management thinks we are all stupid. We are not smart enough to make good decisions." Can it be any wonder that workers are not too eager to submit improvement suggestions when they know their suggestions will never be implemented? Kaizen changes the paradigms of management. Leaders are responsible to solicit contributions and suggestions and implement them while enthusiasm is high and critics have not had time to object.

Organization, cleanliness, cooperation, communication, and training are all intangible assets, which are difficult to measure or quantify, but essential to the success of kaizen. Companies using the Toyota Production System understand it is everyone's job to make improvements on their jobs on a regular basis. Kaizen is a process that allows "good ideas" to become reality— ideas that team members submit as part of the continuous improvement process. With the new tools of lean, all answers come from within. Kaizen unlocks the talents and abilities of workers and allows decisions to be made at the lowest level in the organization, in the quickest time, by the people who know the situation best. The Toyota Production System forces workers to operate as teams, thus creating a synergy that is absent in most normal workplaces. This energy allows much more to be accomplished as a team than as individual workers.

In the United States, kaizen usually refers to an event of from three to five days. It is comprised of intensive improvement activities directed at specific areas of a business. It may be called a "blitz," "five days and one night," "gemba kaizen," "blitz kaizen," "system kaizen," or "breakthrough kaizen." Whatever the name, it is a process based on improving quality, cost, and delivery by the elimination of waste (muda). Its main goals are the implementation of one-piece flow, working to takt time, and development of a pull system.

A kaizen event is a means to accelerate improvements that increase worker productivity, helping management find new ways to gain substantial savings in time, space, and labor output. Kaizen is never meant to be the method of getting rid of workers; instead it is a tool of growth Focused on results, kaizen has been shown to collapse lead times, dramatically reduce work in process, and reduce scrap and defects while minimizing the need for capital expenditures. The results are real, proven, documented, and confirmed!

THE TOYOTA PRODUCTION SYSTEM

The Toyota Production System (TPS) is based on being *lean*. Its mantra is to manufacture only what is needed by the customer, when it is needed, and in the quantities ordered. The manufacture of these goods is done in a way that minimizes the time to deliver the finished goods, the amount of labor, and amount of floor space—while achieving the highest quality at the lowest cost. Time saved is the key measure of cost and efficiency in TPS. Kaizen seeks to minimize throughput time by eliminating non-value-added activities.

But TPS is more than just a new way to make things in a factory. It must be driven by a new way of thinking, which brings about cultural change. By thinking "lean," everyone becomes involved in the elimination of waste, in all of its forms, at all levels, all the time. Workers are empowered to make changes and have a voice in the decision-making process. Flexibility, simplicity and the quest for constant improvement become the driving goals in the new lean operation.

TPS Tools

The Toyota Production System changes manufacturing from traditional, large batch, lot processing to product-based, one-at-a-time flow production. In undertaking this transformation, it is the guide by which lean manufacturing is achieved. The Toyota Production System uses many individual tools, including:

- kanban,
- jidoka,
- total quality management (TQM),
- total productive maintenance (TPM),
- single-minute exchange of dies (SMED),
- 5S (sort, shine, standardize, set in order, sustain)
- visual factory,
- cause-and-effect diagram with the addition of cards (CEDAC),
- hoshin kanri,
- andon,
- poka-yoke,
- 5 why analysis,
- the elimination of waste (muda), and

• constant teaching and training of the work force.

Kaizen uses these tools to model a new manufacturing process—one that is based on cells and just-in-time flow. Cells are representative of product families—parts that can be manufactured complete—as opposed to the traditional groupings of processes that manufacture many different products. The formation of cells creates mini factories-within-a-factory to make complete products.

The new shop floor cells use minimum in-process inventory and a pull system for inventory control. Thus most common problems are easily exposed. They are then fixed or minimized and improvements are immediately realized.

CHANGE

When it comes to dealing with change, each business is unique and so is each person. But change is a fact of life, and to gain acceptance, each situation must be adapted to the most suitable condition given the circumstances, which will bring about the best possible result. There is no substitute for common sense and prudent judgment in the implementation of kaizen. This manual will point you in the right direction as you begin your journey.

One

The History of Lean

FOUNDING THE TOYOTA PRODUCTION SYSTEM

In 1922, Sakiichi Toyoda, an engineer, humbly started out in the textile business. A few years later he developed the first automatic loom, which allowed for tremendous and continued growth in the Toyoda textile business until the beginning of WWII.

Meanwhile, in Detroit, Michigan, Henry Ford had devised the first moving assembly lines. Ford was continuously working to reduce the manufacturing time required to build a car. As a result of improvements, the time was reduced from 728 minutes to 93 minutes per car by 1927. The retail price of a car went from $950 in 1908 to $290 in 1927!

Kiichiro Toyoda visited the Ford Rouge Plant in 1929 to view the successful operation first-hand. There he observed a completely self-contained manufacturing operation.

In 1930, Toyota was asked to produce special vehicles for the Japanese government. To forward this venture into automotive manufacture, Taiichi Ohno was hired in 1932 as a product engineer.

In 1937, Kiichiro Toyoda was faced with a big decision—whether or not to seriously continue in the automotive manufacturing business. He remembered his visit to the Ford Motor Company. That visit was to influence his decision to continue automotive manufacture at Toyota. Kiichiro Toyoda relayed his observations from the Ford Motor Company visit to Taiichi Ohno. However, both realized that the investment required to emulate Ford's Rouge facility was beyond the meager means of the new Toyota Motor Company. Mr. Ohno's challenge was to imitate Ford, but with far, far less. Better ways that did not require vast cash resources would have to be found.

At the outbreak of WWII, the company's production shifted from textile equipment to heavy vehicles for the war effort. After the war, Toyota Motor Company floundered. Because of the collapsed Japanese economy, sales were almost zero, and the company was on the brink of bankruptcy.

Soichiro Honda founded the Honda Motor Company in 1948. He was searching for the right combination of theories and processes to grow his company. He too studied all the available information on manufacturing. It is not known for sure, but speculation has it that there were discussions among Honda, Matsushita, and Toyoda regarding the best way to mass produce. They discovered that there were some very promising ideas abounding.

In 1949, Toyota laid off 25% of its workers just to survive. This caused a worker strike, which was only settled when Kiichiro Toyoda resigned, predicating that his mismanagement was responsible for the company's problems. The strike was settled when Toyota agreed that from then on, no worker would ever lose his job. A worker had a job for life, and workers agreed to help the company in return by doing what they could to continuously improve operations.

It was now 1950, and Taiichi Ohno was manager of the Honsha machining plant. His views were developing as he studied the key innovators of the past and present. And within Toyota, Shigeo Shingo was working as an engineering consultant to reduce setup times for stamping dies. He was also working to reduce non-value-added labor. He presented his work, "Production as a Network of Processes and Identification of Lot Delays," to the Japan Management Association.

In 1950, Toyota sold fewer than 3,000 vehicles, which was hardly indicative of what was to come for eventually the world's largest automobile manufacturer. The company was at a crossroads. How could it survive as an automobile manufacturer and be competitive in the world market?

Toyota was not alone in its strive for world competitiveness. All Japanese manufacturers were facing the same problem. Matsushita Electric Company was trying to emulate Ford's concept of mass production. The company reached out to the mass market by lowering prices to drive up sales. Konosuke Matsushita had developed his own theories about management. He too believed in lifelong employment, and that employees should be continually improving all aspects of the business as part of their responsibility to the company. These progressive ideas were implemented at Matsushita. The challenge then was how to make them work. And would they be successful?

Other pioneers were also making their mark on the industrial world by introducing innovative ideas and theories to address manufacturing problems and challenges. These innovators greatly influenced Taiichi Ohno's thinking, as did the results of WWII. He was contemplating

what would serve Toyota best. Again, he considered what he had seen at the Ford Rouge plant. Could Toyota copy Ford's production system? Probably not. The Ford system required much more capital than Toyota could afford. So he sought other options.

Taiichi Ohno looked at all the available literature and found a 1912 translation of Frederick W. Taylor's, *Shop Management* (Taylor 1911). After more investigating he found more material by Taylor, all of which contained exactly what he was looking for—ways to become more efficient. He found that in 1915 Taylor's theories had been tried at Niigata Engineering's Kamath, Japan plant. Taiichi studied other Japanese translations of American works, including Toshiro Ikeda's "Secret of Eliminating Unprofitable Efforts" from 1925, which was another of Frederick Taylor's works (Ikeda 1925). He also looked at Lillian and Frank Gilbreth's studies on "efficiency." There were many ideas to choose from. This exhaustive and continuing investigation provided him with some basic tools for developing his own "Toyota Production System." But where would he begin?

Japanese businesses struggled to become competitive, seeking more information on how to eliminate non-value added activities and become more efficient. Many American publications were translated and read by the major Japanese business owners. The concept of methods, time, measurements (MTM) was introduced in 1948 (Maynard et al. 1948). Larry D. Miles introduced value analysis at General Electric (Miles 1961). And, Marvin E. Mundel and Ralph Barnes were publishing motion and time study books (Mundel 1985; Barnes 1949).

As manager of machining at the Honsha plant, we know Taiichi Ohno experimented with many ideas, not only those of others, but his own, determining what worked and what did not. What worked became known as the Toyota Production System (TPS).

Taiichi Ohno said, "TPS has a strong feature of emphasizing practical effects and actual practice and implementation over theoretical analysis." He believed success was determined on the shop floor, through trial and error, as opposed to acceptance based on theory alone.

INFLUENCE OF AMERICAN QUALITY EXPERTS

The basic rules and concepts of the Toyota Production System were just coming together when a new twist was added. Along came Dr. W. Edwards Deming, Dr. W. A. Shewhart, and Joseph Juran. In 1950, as part of the post-WWII effort to rebuild Japan, Dr. Deming traveled there to advise and train Japanese manufacturers on quality. (Dr. Shewhart was too busy.)

Most of Japan's early imports to America were cheap, poorly made, and lacked quality. Dr. Deming spent considerable time in Japan teaching companies about statistics and quality, advising them on how to apply the concepts to make good products. He has been called the creator of the "Japanese Industrial Miracle."

In the same time frame, Joseph Juran conceptualized the Pareto principle and published his *Quality Control Handbook* (Juran 1951). He also lectured throughout Japan, teaching "quality" to business and industry.

Juran and Deming remain highly regarded by Japanese business and industry. In 1951, the highest quality award in Japan was named after Dr. Deming and is called the Deming Prize.

As a result of the work of Dr. Deming and Joseph Juran, Japan established "inductive statistical quality control" as a standard for quality. At first, Juran and Deming only instructed company management on this standard. It was not until 1961 that this same training was administered to shop-floor personnel.

WORLD MARKET COMPETITION

Meanwhile Taiichi Ohno was further perfecting the Toyota Production System, adding the improvement of Shigeo Shingo's single-minute exchange of die (SMED) technique and later his "pre-automation" concept. Other Japanese manufacturers were also developing their own "lean" methods of manufacturing based on what was taught by Deming and Juran, combined with the initial ideas of Gilbreth and Taylor, all of which were widely known.

The decade of the 1950s was a time of transition for manufacturing. The world economy was good, markets were growing, and new products were being introduced. Competition was fierce.

In 1955, 95% of cars sold in the USA were made in the USA. To penetrate the US market, Toyota was preparing to embark on a 20-year plan to convert all of its manufacturing to the Toyota Production System. Part of this transformation would be carried out by Shigeo Shingo through his lectures on "Separation of Workers and Machines."

By this time, Taiichi Ohno was Vice President of Toyota Motors. He dedicated his life to implementing and perfecting the system he put together from the best ideas the world of business and industry had to offer.

Shigeo Shingo continued his study of industrial engineering and published a study on the scientific thinking mechanism (STM), which was soon followed by additional works.

The year 1960 brought about a milestone event, which energized Toyota to become even more aggressive in its approach to "lean" manufacturing. Nissan won the coveted

Deming Prize for Quality. At this news, Toyota vowed that it too would win the Deming prize. However, it took Toyota until 1965 to earn it.

KAIZEN

In the early 1960s, Shigeo Shingo introduced the concept of zero quality control (ZQC) (source inspection and the poka-yoke system). From his ideas, in 1962, Tetsuichi Asaka and Kaoru Ishikawa developed "quality circles." These resulted in the first real kaizen events. Quality circles focused on solving quality problems that interrupted production throughout the plant. The quality circle was a cross-functional team charged with analyzing and finding the root cause of a problem, formulating a solution, and then implementing it. (Much of the problem solving was done with a cause-and-effect diagram with the addition of cards [CEDAC], which was devised by Kaoru Ishikawa in 1950.) It was with the implementation of quality circles that Toyota won the Deming Prize for Quality in 1965.

In 1962, Masaaki Imai established the Kaizen Institute, which was devoted solely to the promotion of kaizen throughout the world. In the USA, domestic automobile manufacturers were no longer commanding 95% of the domestic market. This statistic was to only get worse.

The 1960s spawned significant new advances in the field of management in the USA. Maynard published the *Industrial Engineering Handbook*, which was one of the first works to recognize that the Japanese had indeed developed systems that were different and better than what was currently used in most American factories (Maynard 1963).

Various other books delved into the inner motivation of workers (Nadler 1963; Maslow 1970; Herzberg 1966; Roethlisberger 1968). Many American companies were basing their management styles on these new theories.

Meanwhile Toyota and other Japanese companies were getting stronger and more competitive by perfecting the Toyota Production System, which defied all of the current motivational theories. Ideas were abounding; application and results were to follow. At Toyota, the TPS was widely accepted and employees were making about one suggestion per person per week. Most suggestions were adopted immediately through a kaizen event or casually just as a way of improving the workplace. Kaizen was a success.

THE OIL CRISIS

A major milestone was achieved in 1971. Taiichi Ohno proclaimed that his lifelong ambition to complete the Toyota Production System was achieved. This was just in time for the next major event, the oil embargo, which would establish Toyota and the Japanese as formidable competitors in the world automobile market. The oil crisis forced the Japanese, who import 100% of their oil, to get even leaner so they could continue manufacturing and competing in world markets. Everywhere in companies large and small there was the need to "kaizen" everything to survive, to make do with less, sometimes almost nothing. The real value of kaizen was realized. The culture accepted kaizen. And it worked!

In the USA the oil crisis was weathered, but not without a lot of new rules, laws, and mandates. Speed limits were lowered to 55 mph. There were mandates to the American automobile manufacturers to make fuel-efficient vehicles.

The Japanese had the same challenges, but they had the advantage of the Toyota Production System, the Nissan Production System, the Mazda Production System, the Matsushita System, etc.

The oil crisis meant an overall reduction in sales of larger, less fuel-efficient vehicles; it meant more engineering and, of course, added costs. The race was on between the Japanese and the Americans to develop fuel-efficient cars. But the Japanese cars were already much more fuel efficient, and they were cheaper to buy and operate. Sales of Japanese cars in the USA exploded. Japan was now in the driver's seat.

EMULATING THE JAPANESE

American manufacturers scrambled to copy from the Japanese. But the know-how was not available in any book. So, in 1979 Ford bought a 25% stake in Mazda to learn firsthand how to become lean. Some US companies formed partnerships with Japanese companies. And others scrambled to learn all they could from wherever they could so they might try to implement their own version of whatever was making the Japanese successful.

In Japan, the assorted manufacturing systems were getting even better. Shigeo Shingo had introduced the nonstock production system (NSP-S) and published his concepts in books (Shingo 1985, 1986, 1988, 1989). Further, Matsushita developed the Mikuni Method, a derivation of the Toyota Production System.

Consultants such as Imai were overwhelmed with opportunities in the USA to train companies on the use of the Toyota Production System through kaizen events. Japanese consulting companies were partnering with American consulting companies. Shingijutsu, founded in 1987 and associated with Productivity, Inc., was the first to offer Americans a chance to travel to Japan to see first-hand how the Japanese were applying the Toyota Production System and lean manufacturing.

Today there are many tools that originated within TPS. They are: kaizen events, kanban, jidoka, total quality management (TQM), total productive maintenance (TPM), single-minute exchange of dies (SMED), 5S (straighten, sort, shine, standardize, sustain), the visual factory, cause-and-effect diagrams with the addition of cards (CEDAC), hoshin-kanri, andon, poka-yoke, the elimination of muda (waste), and constant teaching and training of the workforce.

REFERENCES

Barnes, Ralph M. 1949. *Motion and Time Study*, 3rd Edition. New York: J. Wiley.

Herzberg, Frederick. 1966. *Work and the Nature of Man*. Cleveland, OH: World Publishing Company.

Ikeda, Toshiro. 1925. Japanese translation of *Secret of Eliminating Unprofitable Efforts. Noritsu Zoshin Mueki No Tesu o Habuku Hiketsu*. Tokyo, Japan: Efishenshi Kyokai, Manejimentosha, Taisho.

Kaizen Express

Juran, Joseph M. 1951. *Quality Control Handbook*. New York: McGraw-Hill.

Maslow, Abraham H. 1970. *Motivation and Personality*, 2nd Edition. New York: Harper & Row.

Maynard, H. B., Stegemerten, G. J., and Schwab, J. L. 1948. *Methods-Time Measurement*. New York: McGraw-Hill Book Company.

Maynard, H. B. 1963. *Industrial Engineering Handbook*, 2nd Edition. New York: McGraw-Hill.

Miles, Lawrence D. 1961. *Techniques of Value Analysis and Engineering*. New York: McGraw-Hill.

Mundel, Marvin E. 1985. *Motion and Time Study: Improving Productivity*, 6th Edition. Englewood Cliffs, NJ: Prentice-Hall.

Nadler, Gerald. 1963. *Work Design*. Homewood, IL: R. D. Irwin.

Roethlisberger, F. J. 1968. "Man in Organization" essays. Cambridge: Belknap Press of Harvard University Press.

Shingo, Shigeo. 1985. *A Revolution in Manufacturing: The SMED System*. Stamford, CT: Productivity Press.

Shingo, Shigeo. 1986. *Zero Quality Control: Source Inspection and the Poka-yoke System*. Cambridge, MA: Productivity Press.

Shingo, Shigeo, 1988. *Nonstock Production: the Shingo System for Continuous Improvement*. Cambridge, MA: Productivity Press.

Shingo, Shigeo. 1989. *A Study of the Toyota Production System from an Industrial Engineering Viewpoint*. Cambridge, MA: Productivity Press.

Taylor, Frederick W. 1911. *Shop Management*. New York, London: Harper & Brothers.

Two

Toyota Production System Training

TRAINING METHODS

There are as many ways to train people as there are people. Some just seem to have a better knack than others when it comes to training and teaching. Just what is it that they have or do that is better? Can there be a "best" way to train?

The Japanese think so. They rediscovered the Training Within Industry (TWI) technique, which was originally developed by the U.S. government during WWII to bring an inexperienced workforce up to speed quickly. It was introduced to Japan in the postwar construction period and adopted by Taiichi Ohno as one of the foundations he used to build the Toyota Production System (TPS).

The TWI technique is as applicable in classrooms as it is out on the production floor. Inclusive of TWI, the Toyota Production System only uses the best possible training methodologies that have proven to be unsurpassed in the world. In fact, they mandate that all training be done only one way with no deviation or exceptions. They have discovered what works best and use the specific techniques extensively.

Before reading about how the TPS handles training, here is a list of the methods that *do not* work.

- Buddy system—I sit next to you, watch you, and what you know migrates to me.

- Read all about it—Read the "how to do this" manual. "By the way, I skipped a few pages that were boring or that I did not understand."

- Class full of "rookies"—No one has been prescreened. Students do not know about TPS or teaming, and are not committed.

- Fast learner—"Here, let me do it my way. I can do anything!"

Companies that practice the TPS method of training have a distinct advantage over those who do not. They are prepared and ready to service customers faster and at a lower cost, and thus are able to attract new customers who previously belonged to the competition.

"Train the Trainer" Team Leader Training

Usually, a consultant conducts the first few kaizen events in a company. In doing so, he or she typically conducts a special training session specifically for team leaders. It is recommended that all aspiring team leaders attend this preliminary training to prepare them for their future roles. As team leaders, they will be expected to know how to conduct Toyota Production System (TPS) training for team members prior to every event.

"Train the trainer" is the Japanese standardized method of guaranteeing that a student will positively learn what is being taught. Those who have used "train the trainer" methods can attest to the fact that they indeed work—every time!

The TPS method of training, not previously translated into English, is what all Toyota trainers use as a standard. The training generally takes one full day and accomplishes two objectives: 1) The trainer learns the TPS method of training; and 2) A typical subject or process is used to train with, so as the "subject" is covered, flaws in the process are discovered and corrected. The net results are a process is perfected; a trainer is trained; and a standard methodology is established for the training process. And, because actual subjects or processes are used, the training is customized to the needs of the organization.

The TPS Method

The TPS method of training is proven and is the format all trainers must use. As the trainer delivers the TPS material, the following key personal qualities and values must be emphasized to all the students:

1. They must be committed. Everyone must believe the new philosophies of TPS 100%—no exceptions—no reluctance.

2. The value of time must be understood and appreciated. Time is the most valuable element of business. The sense of urgency must be appreciated and the importance stressed.

3. Each person must practice internal discipline to complete a task, stay on course, and not give up. Without internal discipline, external discipline must be exercised, which is counterproductive. External discipline comprises the laws and rules that exert public pressure to conform.

The following sections contain step-by-step instructions for the trainer to use when administering TPS training.

Stage I: Prepare for Learning

1. Introduce yourself as the trainer. Ask about the students' personal likes and hobbies, families, etc. Find out what they know or have heard about TPS. Ask about their jobs. Make them feel at ease, like part of a family.

2. Explain about the operation they will be learning. Tell them that as their trainer, you will help them in any way needed.

3. Ask if they have previous experience in the operation. Have the students show you how they currently do it. Tell them there may be some differences between the way they now do a task and the way it will be done in the future. Mention why the TPS requires that there be only one way to do a task, and that what they are being instructed to do is the best method.

4. Motivate the students. Explain to them of the importance of the operation and define the critical elements. Tell them how each task fits into the overall picture.

5. Place the students in the correct starting position. That is, be aware of ergonomics, of their height and body size. Make them feel comfortable.

Explain that most jobs require standing, why it is healthier for the worker to be mobile, and how the requirements of the job dictate the worker be mobile—hence no sitting.

6. Express the need for safety. Make sure there are no unresolved safety issues.

Stage II: Explain the Operation

1. Demonstrate how to do the operation. Explain every detail as you go along. Explain why the sequence is as such. Express what might happen if the exact sequence is not followed. Make it clear why the Standard Work Combination Sheets are always followed and how they document the details of the process.

2. Element by element, get the students familiar with the operation.

3. Demonstrate how to do the process again. Match the emphasized key points with the corresponding physical motions.

4. Demonstrate how to do it again. But this time, show the reasoning behind each key point and explain the consequences if it is not followed exactly.

5. Do not give students more than they can handle. Let them completely master each element of the operation before moving on. Explain that the sequence of learning requires each step be perfected before continuing to the next or increasing the speed.

6. Use patience. Go slowly and steadily. Let the students gain the confidence that they have mastered each element.

Stage III: Practice

1. Let the students do the operation. Check to see if they follow instructions correctly. Correct errors as they occur. Use language such as, "This way brings a better consistent result," or "This way is safer."

2. Let the students continue. See if they can recite the given procedure while performing the operation.

3. Let the students do it again. But this time ask them to recite the key points. Let them

refer to the key points as they do the task. Ask questions as they explain. Be certain they understand the key points.

4. Let the students repeat it again. Have them explain in detail the reason for the sequence, the key points, and caveats to not following the exact sequence or process. Compliment them for doing a good job when they finally do it exactly right. Be patient.

Stage IV: Consolidate

1. Let the students do the operation alone. Now have them do an actual job. Stress quality before quantity. They must learn how to make perfect parts before they accelerate the pace.

2. Explain that they must always refer to the trainer for answers to questions about the process or the way it is done.

3. Check again and give follow-up advice.

4. Tell the students to feel free to ask questions. Make them feel comfortable.

5. The final step is to have each student assume the role of trainer. Have him or her go through the same procedure witnessed as when a student. Observe and make comments as required.

6. When the student has progressed to the point that you feel they are ready for production, let them loose!

7. On the training matrix, complete the scoring column for each individual to show that he or she is now qualified to do the task.

8. Compliment the student and record the accomplishment on his or her personnel record.

Team Training

The entire kaizen team is required to attend TPS training prior to participating in the event. The training is planned to take place all day Monday and a half-day on Tuesday, if required.

It is preferred that all team members be active in their participation in the training, even if they have attended TPS training before. When someone is attending for the second or third time, these team members should be asked to co-lead the team and assist the team leader whenever possible. There is more than enough work for everyone.

Occasionally, someone may audit or monitor the class for reasons that might not be clear to the team leader or the rest of the team. These auditors should be quiet and inconspicuous, since they are not considered part of the team.

During the training, sufficient time should be allowed for the students to practice via hands-on exercises. For instance, to demonstrate the preferred method of using a stopwatch during a time study, the watch is kept running while one team member calls out the time when an element of the process begins, which is immediately written on the observation sheet by another person. Learning by doing is the Toyota method.

The instructional outline for TPS team training is as follows:

- conducting a time study,
- making a spaghetti diagram,
- computing takt time and making a graph,
- determining the value-added ratio,
- reviewing the process capacity table,
- using the Standard Work Combination Sheets,
- determining standard work layouts, and
- optimizing the new cell.

Conducting a Time Study

The current-state value stream map is highlighted to point out where improvement is needed in the work and information flow. Once the target areas are selected, the details must be planned and executed. Each target area is time-studied to establish a benchmark and verify the process as it is supposed to be performed. If it is not performed as it should be, the process must be corrected, re-executed, and realistic times recorded. For example, there may be tools or machines in the area that are missing or not functioning properly. They must be repaired or replaced so the process will function as originally designed. More information on conducting a time study can be found in Chapter 7.

Making a Spaghetti Diagram

The next preliminary action is to measure out the actual distance a part moves as it progresses from station to station until completed and construct a spaghetti diagram (refer to Chapter 7). The distance an operator has to move with the processes is also measured. If multiple operators are part of the current cell, all have to be measured independently.

Computing Takt Time and Making a Graph

Sometimes in a new lean cell it may be possible to eliminate all but one of the current operators. This should be the goal—maximum efficiency. Working to takt time is not as important as determining the most efficient method of production when redesigning a process. The most efficient manufacturing process is one that uses the least amount of resources to output the most product; thus it is the quickest at the least cost. Takt time requirements are then used to balance the process. (Refer to Chapter 7 for further information on computing takt time and making a graph.)

Determining the Value-added Ratio

Once the best process is designed and the takt time requirements determined, the value-added ratio can be calculated. (See Chapter 7 for how to do this.)

Reviewing the Process Capacity Table

The process capacity table is reviewed to be sure information is correct. (Chapter 7 shows an example).

Using the Standard Work Combination Sheets

Once the new lean cell is implemented and ISO requirements fulfilled, the Standard Work Combination Sheets is completed. (See Chapter 7 for an example and instructions on its use.)

Determining Standard Work Layouts

Standard Work Layout Sheets diagram the work steps as they must be performed. (Chapter 7 contains an example.)

Optimizing the New Cell

Operators must be trained on how to run the new cell. They also must have knowledge of 5S practice and evaluation; how to track and post the appropriate metrics; and total productive maintenance (TPM).

For the first three days, minute-to-minute operation of the cell is closely monitored. Problems are noted and appropriate adjustments are made on the fly to allow the cell to attain the expected improvements. The operator's movements are also refined.

At the end of the first week there is a complete debriefing, which includes the operator, maintenance people, supervisor, and anyone else who is part of the cell, to evaluate and critique everything. Ongoing adjustments, both physical and otherwise, are made to improve the cell's operation. There is no end to the improvements that can made. Workers should not be satisfied with attaining one level of improvement; raise the bar, shoot for the moon!

THE TOYOTA PRODUCTION SYSTEM

Though TPS has been applied in many world-class companies, many of its tools and philosophies are not yet understood or practiced by business leaders worldwide.

Continuous improvement is one element that is least understood and practiced. In the Toyota Production System, the vast majority of improvements are 85% psychological, and these ideas in turn drive the physical actions and results that most people recognize as the visual aspect of lean. The physical differences are somewhat easy to see when compared to most normal non-TPS businesses, but the philosophical differences are quite subtle.

The following sections detail the cultural as well as physical aspects of Toyota's methodology.

A New Way of Thinking

The Toyota Production System involves a new way of thinking: a way that is by the people, with the people, and for the people. Encouraging empowerment, it allows decision-making at the lowest level, by those who know the process best. The goal is to sufficiently train workers so they possess the proper skills and tools to allow them to make the correct decisions.

Time is the most important element of business. It is the measure of efficiency and competitiveness. It is how a company gains advantage over the competition. It is a company's number one weapon against cost. Therefore, eliminating waste (the Japanese call it "muda") in all its forms is the mantra of everyone. Any activity that takes unnecessary time and resources and adds no value to the activity or product is considered waste.

The theory of participative management encourages everyone to work on teams. The synergy created gives greater results than the sum of the individuals. However, as a member of a team, quality means taking responsibility for each and every part you make or activity you do. Empowerment means you have complete control of stopping the process or activity until corrections are made. Employing the concept of kaizen, or continuous improvement, is an integral component of every employee's responsibility. With the tools of TPS it is possible to standardize the method in which employees are made productive.

The 14 Concepts

This section describes the 14 philosophies, which are the foundation of the Toyota Production System.

They are broad and not too different than what many businesses know and do themselves. But the difference is in the way they should be administered, which is very different than what most businesses practice. There are many more important details to the application of these philosophies. They are discussed in greater depth in related textbooks.

1. *Genchi Genbutsu Shugi*

The English translation of the Japanese phrase "genchi genbutsu shugi" means "practical, hands-on experience is valued over theoretical knowledge." This mandates that all leaders, supervisors, and managers must lead by example on the shop floor or in the middle of the action, and not remotely from an office far removed from the worksite.

2. *Visual Management*

The second concept requires sufficient visual management of processes. Visual tools are used to monitor the key metrics that track production progress and quality. Examples include charts, graphs, pictures, and videos, such as:

- Production Analysis Sheets, which track the reasons for

slow-downs or problems. This tool makes it easy to see where kaizen events will have the most impact.

- Line Productivity Control Sheets, which track daily changes of productivity, defect ratios, availability, etc. They are used to adjust resources and overtime to achieve the daily takt time. (*Takt* is the German word for beat or pace at which production must happen to satisfy the daily production needs of the customer. It is the daily production schedule.)

- Statistical Process Control (SPC) Charts, which track the process to ensure it is stable. This tool is *not* used to check parts for conformity. If the process shows a trend that indicates a deviant part may be made, the process is stopped automatically or manually by the operator before it happens.

- Multi-skilled Map or Skills Matrix, which shows each operator's training and abilities as they apply to the job at hand. This tool also enables scheduling additional training as the needs of the area and individual change.

- Quality Check Sample Table and Check Sheets, which allow the current processes to be monitored continuously by management and the customer.

3. Determine What is Normal or Abnormal

The following tools help track abnormalities in processes, machine performance, and parts. All results are graphed for later comparison to determine negative trends, isolate problems, and bring them under control.

- Check Sheets are used to compare production amounts. These are completed on an hour-by-hour basis, noting any problems with production or quality.

- Performance Check Sheets are used to track machine performance. Every time there is a stoppage, it must be explained in detail. The stoppages are later analyzed and kaizen events are done to eliminate the problems.

- Quality Check Sheets are used to verify part attributes. These are diagrams that list the critical dimensional attributes of a part that must be produced within specified tolerances.

4. Maintenance

Total productive maintenance (TPM) must be in place to keep processes stable. Machines must always produce at the level for which they were designed. The speed, feed, tooling changes, and adjustments are tracked. Optimum settings are standardized and maintained. There must be a baseline for each process and machine so it may be referred to should catastrophic failure occur or the need for major repairs arise.

TPM requires operators to continually monitor and adjust machines in between regularly scheduled maintenance. This includes making sure there is adequate lubrication and performing minor adjustments to maintain a continuous level of production at 100% quality.

5. Kaizen

Kaizen is the concept of continuous improvement. It is used to effect changes on anything that can be improved: process, design, movement, material, assembly, etc. There are three levels of kaizen.

- *Work operation kaizen* involves changes done by the operator to his or her own machine or process, simply, cheaply, immediately, and with little impact on surrounding people or processes. It is the first choice to implement.

- *Kaizen equipment* involves improvements made to a machine or piece of equipment, which requires more time, cost, and resources than a work operation kaizen, and it may affect other people and processes.

- *Process kaizen* affects the complete manufacturing process, and may even affect all the equipment in a process. It may be done to greatly increase production capacity, incorporate engineering changes, or eliminate cost and time. Usually this type of kaizen is conducted when the plan is to develop cells and transform from batch to one-piece flow production.

6. Find Problems

To find problems, the accumulated base data is reviewed, visually confirmed, and analyzed using statistical methods such as *six sigma*. Analysis of data, along with actually viewing a problem, provides the basis for discovery of solutions.

7. Leadership by Example

Referring back to the first concept, "genchi genbutsu shugi," practical, hands-on experience is valued over theoretical knowledge. As applied to leadership by example, workers will follow good, skilled leaders. However, they may not be required to "go where they are told to go" by supervisors who bark orders and lack leadership skills. Leadership by example requires obedience to training and the persistence to concentrate on not making the same mistakes again. Individuals must use Five Why analysis as they try to solve problems. That is, they must continually ask, "why?" until the root cause of the problem is discovered.

8. 5S

There are five Japanese words that describe the basic elements of 5S organization. The words and their English translations are as follows.

- *Seiri* (simplify)—remove all unnecessary clutter from a work area. Keep only what is needed. This allows for the smooth flow of goods. The work area is clear of distractions and there are no hiding places for unused raw material or tools. The area is safer and organized.

- *Seiton* (set in order)—organize items neatly and label them clearly. This reduces the time necessary to find tools and items needed for production. It facilitates the single-minute exchange of dies (SMED) or tools (changeover on a machine in less than 10 minutes).

- *Seiso* (scrub and shine)—make the worksite pleasant and allow for equipment to be checked as it is cleaned. This also relates back to concept one, "genchi genbutsu shugi," know and see, first-hand, the work area.

- *Seiketsu* (stabilize and standardize)—Keep the area clean and neat in appearance. The first step in maintaining a quality production facility is to have the equipment spotless. Establish uniformity. Paint lines on the floor to show aisles, parking, and locations of items, tools and equipment used in the area, or to show limits and indicate danger. "Everything is in its place—and there is a place for everything."

- *Shitsuke* (sustain)—Instill discipline in everyone to follow the rules and maintain all of the Ss without fail. This involves a cultural change—accepting the importance of cleanliness in the workplace.

- Some American companies add a sixth S—safety.

These elements are implemented in order with seiri occurring first and culminating with shitsuke. It is customary to do a weekly 5S assessment of each work area and post the results in the information station at each department. It is assumed that each area will strive to improve their scores. This is part of the continuous improvement culture, which drives the physical activities.

9. Safety

Safety is the first priority of the supervisor. He or she is responsible to ensure everyone on the team knows and understands the aspects of working safely. Team members must obey all safety rules.

10. Cross-train

A skills matrix is maintained for each team, which shows who was trained and to what level, the jobs each person is capable of doing, and the schedule for future training. Training is emphasized in all areas of Japanese business. It is perceived as an investment in the future of the company. Employees who are taught the right philosophies will practice those skills. The reward will be a lean organization where muda is minimized and time is valued.

The more job skills a worker attains, the more value he or she is to the company. The more jobs a worker can do, the more he or she is paid under the Toyota Production System.

11. Self-education

Team members should strive to better themselves. Because there is incentive (more pay), workers enthusiastically pursue cross-training in all workplace tasks. Some team members aspire to take team leader training and team leaders aspire to take group leader training, and so on. Everyone should be contributing kaizen suggestions regularly and implementing them as a normal part of daily work.

12. Teams

Everyone working on teams creates synergy, resulting in greater contributions than the sum of individual efforts. There is an old proverb in Japan that translated states, "The nail that sticks up is the one that gets pounded down." Applied here, this basically means "individualists" are not wanted. Only "team members" are welcome.

13. Communication

Communication is important. It begins with the team. One benefit of teaming is that each member knows as much about a given situation as the next. The team leader has the task of ensuring all team members are informed. He or she must create an atmosphere of honesty and trust. Everyone must trust one another, the team leader, group leader, management, and workers. The whole organization is more like a family than a workplace.

14. Quality Circle

The actual origin of U.S. "quality" programs, Ford Motor copied the quality circle methodology seen in Japanese factories. Ford thought (wrongly) that quality circles were the answer to why Japanese companies did so well. It was assumed that the sole outcome of Deming training was the formation of quality circles. Ford came to realize there was a lot more to it!

In the Toyota Production System, each employee has a common goal to work with others on a team, cooperate, and help one another. Supervisors must foster an atmosphere where subordinates can discuss issues and know that management will listen and act on their suggestions and ideas. The quality circle is a key tool that forces the correct actions to take place in the proper sequence and without deviation. A quality circle performs the following tasks:

- *Plan*: first identify problems and analyze them. Then make an improvement plan for their countermeasures.

- *Do*: implement the plan.

- *Check*: verify and evaluate the results.

- *Act*: consider the standardization and permanent adoption or next countermeasure.

Seven Basic Tools of Quality

There are seven basic tools of quality used in the Toyota Production System. Their function involves the collection and manipulation of data.

1. *Histogram*—A bar graph that shows frequency data, it provides an easy, visual way to

evaluate and compare data distribution.

2. *Pareto Diagram*—This is a histogram aided by the 80/20 rule—approximately 80% of problems are created by 20% of the causes. It is used to identify and prioritize problems.

3. *Cause and Effect Diagram*—also called the Ishikawa Diagram or Fishbone Diagram, it is used to discover all the possible causes for a particular effect. It is the first step to effective problem solving as it creates a list of possible causes to investigate and allows the examination of worst-case scenarios.

4. *Run Chart*—With data arranged according to time or order, it is used to analyze processes by tracking variations along a timeline.

5. *Scatter Diagram*—Tracking data from the observation of two different sets of variables, it is used to study and identify the possible relationships between the pieces of data. For instance, it may be used to determine the rela-

tionship of machine speed to the number of completed parts: "If a machine's speed is increased, how many more parts will it make?"

6. *Flow Chart*—A pictorial representation showing all of the steps in a process, there are many variations to this type of chart. Some show information flow and others may use a computer program to generate a chart showing process sequence.

7. *Control Chart*—Used extensively as a quality-reporting chart along with statistical process control (SPC), it allows a process to be reviewed to see if it is within acceptable tolerances. It also can be used to determine whether a process will produce a service or product with consistent measurable properties.

Problem Solving

Once the seven tools of quality are understood, they can be applied to problem solving. They enable workers to make the right decisions, spontaneously, and at the lowest level. Empowerment is a main tenet of the Toyota Production System.

The TPS methodology of problem solving is as follows.

1. *Understand the current condition.* Identify the problem. Use the seven tools of quality to quantify the data. Evaluate and prioritize the data as to its importance.

2. *Set a goal.* Again, the manipulation of the data will help determine the priorities. A definite deadline must be established. Look to make enough improvements so they will pay for themselves. Know the return-on-investment schedule.

3. *Analyze the relationship between the problem and the cause.* You must get to the absolute root of the cause; otherwise the solution will not fit the problem.

4. *Draft a countermeasure.* Build a matrix of the countermeasures, including the advantages and limitations for each. Choose the countermeasure that clearly has the advantage over the others. Use a Process Control Chart, such as a Gantt Chart, to track the progress.

5. *Implement the plan.* Follow progress with the Gantt Chart, making adjustments as needed.

6. *Check for effectiveness.* Determine if adjustments are effective by tracking results with the Gantt Chart. Any negative items must be resolved immediately. Do not move on until open issues are resolved.

7. *Standardize and try other options as needed.* When the countermeasures work, document them and make them permanent. Do not forget to follow QS9000/ISO 9000 documentation procedures. Add up the savings and maintain a history of accumulated results.

Three

Kaizen Worldwide

IMPLEMENTATION

Kaizen has been implemented in just about every country that manufactures throughout the world. Not dependent on the language or education level of the workforce, it has been mastered by company presidents as well as entry-level workers.

Previous knowledge of manufacturing or a special formula is not required to implement kaizen. However, it does require an open mind and a willingness to try anything. The thinking is, it is better to try and fail than to wait for the perfect time to begin. Failures are a sign of learning and trying. (And there is no finger pointing or blame if an idea should fail.)

TEAMS AND RECOGNITION

A kaizen event offers an immediate opportunity for workers to become team members. Everyone likes to be a member of a team. Good things get even better when they can be shared. All team members are considered equal and everyone has a chance to contribute. There are no ranks, no politics, and implementation of ideas is immediate. All ideas are good. And, the hard work not only benefits the company, but the workers themselves, making their jobs easier. Everybody wins!

Recognition is a highly successful motivator appreciated by everyone. It gives some workers the chance to be recognized, whereas in the normal course of their daily job, there is no chance for recognition. One of the great and wonderful effects of kaizen events is the discovery of "diamonds-in-the-rough"—previously unrecognized kaizen heroes.

CULTURAL CHANGE

Kaizen involves cultural change before it is physically implemented. It has been said by the originators at Toyota that 80% of the journey to lean is learning and living the new philosophy, and 20% is changing things physically to accommodate the new way of thinking. Since kaizen is new to most of the workforce, the difficulty of acceptance lies with no specific group; nor is understanding more difficult for any one in particular. The only caveat is that people with closed minds can be difficult to "convert."

Workers who say, "If it ain't broke, don't fix it!" Or, "We've been doing this forever and it was okay, why change now?" tend to have closed minds to change. People fear the unknown more than anything. Kaizen and the changes it brings are unknowns to most doubters. One way to minimize opposition and fear is to get everyone to participate in de-

termining what and where changes should be made. Ideas are for the benefit of the workers and company. When a worker has an idea, he or she takes ownership and is responsible for promoting it and proving it can work. From the worker's standpoint, kaizen is a chance to help yourself where no one would help you before. The key to eliminating fear and reluctance is to educate people on the possibilities and give them the chance to carry out their ideas. This is *participative management*.

The theories and philosophies of lean must be clearly understood and adopted by the workforce so "lean thinking" is instilled in the culture of the organization. Just knowing the technical terms and seeing the physical aspects of the Toyota Production System (TPS) are not enough. Training the workforce to think "lean" is the all-important first step before becoming concerned with the tools. Lean thinking is the catalyst to sustained improvement.

Rearranging the physical locations of machines and equipment will not guarantee a just-in-time flow cell. Workers must understand what is different and why. Decisions should be made by operators because they understand how "lean" works. Lean is not about continuing to do things as they have always been done. It is about eliminating waste in all its forms. This is how processes become efficient. The tools of kaizen allow this to happen quickly, almost immediately!

A UNIVERSAL LANGUAGE

There is universal familiarity with the Toyota Production System and its tools and terminology, which define it. So, in using the tools, their names should remain unchanged. For example, takt time in any language should be takt time; kaizen should remain kaizen; kanban should remain kanban. Using the same terms makes it perfectly clear what is being addressed. The word "kaizen" is used all over the world and people know what it means, even those who are not in manufacturing. This "branding," by using universal terminology, makes it easy for everyone to speak and understand the language of lean.

The smile on a face, the gleam in an eye, tells all that kaizen is a good thing. And this needs no language at all.

Four

Introduction to Kaizen Events

KAIZEN DEFINED

Kaizen is a Japanese word made up of two words, "kai" and "zen." Kai means thinking and zen means good. Together they literally mean continuous improvement.

Kaizen events are a way of accelerating improvements to worker productivity, helping management find new ways to gain substantial savings in time, space, and labor output. Worker ideas are encouraged. Frequent, small improvements result in collapsed lead times, dramatic reductions in work-in-process, and reduced scrap and defects, while minimizing the need for capital expenditures.

Kaizen is not a method for workforce reduction. Instead it is a tool of growth. Personnel not needed should be redeployed or let go prior to beginning the journey to lean. Workers should not be led to think they are leaning themselves out of a job. Their participation is key to the success of kaizen—and it should be made known that status quo is not acceptable. Improvements are personal to the workers, that is, they own the ideas and directly benefit from the improvements. Leaders want these implementers to grow in experience and skills to be of more value to the company.

Barrier Removal

Within an organization, kaizen removes the barriers caused by bureaucracy (red tape) and politics. Kaizen helps a company focus on priorities and allow for progress to happen. It forces cooperation within and between different departments of an organization, improving communications. Kaizen *is* communication.

BENEFITS OF KAIZEN

Kaizen events are important because they provide an excellent return on investment of financial and human resources. And, since kaizen never really ends, continued improvements will compound the return. All ideas should be explored, especially those that need little or no investment to succeed.

Sometimes a kaizen event can eliminate the need for capital equipment expenditure by resolving a bottleneck. When bottlenecks occur, a kaizen event should be done automatically—before considering a new machine purchase. Many times the event results in no new equipment being needed.

Kaizen events often eliminate the need for costly overtime by improving processes while collapsing lead times and dramatically reducing work-in-process. Other immediate results are a reduction in required floor space, reduction in labor, higher quality, faster service for customers, and improved profits.

The flexibility of kaizen events makes them applicable anywhere in the plant, front office to back shipping dock. Wherever there is waste, kaizen can eliminate it.

With every kaizen performed, the training and education of the employees increases, and so does their value to the company. Implementers go forth to promote the methodology of kaizen all around the plant. Quality and morale improves. Respect and trust is built. Good ideas spawn more good ideas. And good results eliminate the fear of failure. Good morale is hard to measure, but attendance usually improves when kaizen is a regular part of everyday activity. Communication also greatly improves at all levels. And, when morale and communication improve, so does safety. In a union shop, grievances decline because there is mutual respect and trust.

KAIZEN REQUIREMENTS

Kaizen events are resource intensive, requiring a team of individuals from the affected area, along with support personnel for its duration. Support for an event is considered top priority so that momentum is not lost. If machines and equipment are to be moved, maintenance personnel are required to facilitate the process, and their involvement will be necessary to reconnect everything afterward. Others that may be called upon to support the event are engineers, setup personnel, forklift drivers, material handlers, and janitors.

During an event, production can be negatively affected by 25% or more. If operators from the production line where the kaizen is occurring are on the kaizen team, their loss, as well as the production stoppages because of the changes, can significantly reduce output. Sometimes it may be necessary to completely shut down a line to make the changes. This shutdown could be for as many as three days. Before a kaizen event occurs, adequate production should be banked to allow for downtime.

Production material must be available to process during the event. Lack of material can make it very difficult, if not impossible, to try out new ideas and measure the improvements.

Changes should be documented as they are made during a kaizen event. Keeping a follow-up list of things to do afterward is recommended. This list must be followed up on to ensure the success of the event.

Sufficient time should be allowed to retrain the operators once the changes are complete. It is also recommended to allow a ramp-up time of at least a week. This is to be sure the new configuration is running consistently at the designed speed and output.

Five

Leading Kaizen Implementation

LEAN CONSULTANT'S ROLE

The lean consultant usually facilitates the first few kaizen events at an organization. These events lay the groundwork and provide training for the champion, management, and workers, who will assume their future roles as trainers, team leaders, and team members on future events. Once experience has been gained, the consultant assumes more of an advisory and mentoring role, overseeing the events until his or her services are no longer needed.

During the event, the consultant is present at each team meeting to evaluate the progress and make suggestions on how to improve. Additional on-the-spot training may be given by the consultant if needed.

The consultant has made certain promises to the client, and he must evaluate if these expectations have been met. If not, then there needs to be an agreement as to the next steps to take. Sometimes a midcourse change is necessary. The team leader or key individuals may not measure up to what is expected in regard to daily accomplishments. This could be because there is not sufficient material to run through the current process to conduct the time studies or prove out the new cell configuration. Or, there may be a lack of cooperation with maintenance. In any case, the goals and objectives of the kaizen event need to change. Based upon the circumstances, the consultant and management may agree that it should become a 5S event instead, and not involve the design of a new cell.

Management Updates

Because the success of kaizen is so important, management usually demands regular updates on the progress. It is a responsibility of the consultant to keep management informed, especially of difficulties, which may alter the outcome of the event. For instance, things may happen that are out of control of the kaizen team, such as not having material to run or not being able to do time studies and measure improvements. If the latter does happen, management needs to know that much of what was timed or measured was estimated. This is important so a decision can be made as to whether or not the team should continue with its current plan. It is quite possible that circumstances could cause a team to change its goals and objectives. For instance, instead of designing cells, a 5S (sort, set in order, shine, standardize, and sustain) event may need to replace the original plan.

Team Leader Meetings

The lean consultant is responsible for conducting team leader meetings during an event. These are held so that a comparison of progress can be made among the teams. Methodologies can be compared and team leaders can adjust team activities appropriately. It is a time for information sharing where team leaders can ask for suggestions and help.

At the end of each day, the consultant facilitates a team leader meeting with all the plant managers. This is a good way to find out if the goals and objectives of the event are being met.

LEAN CHAMPION'S ROLE

In reality, the kaizen event is never complete. Over time, improvements continue to be made and the lean champion must monitor the activity. Annually, it is the responsibility of the lean champion to establish plant priorities for lean training and implementation, and to work with the director of continuous improvement and plant manager to establish a TPS training and kaizen event schedule. On an ongoing basis, the champion is also responsible for:

- establishing and maintaining the product quantity analysis;

- conducting post-mortem meetings after the events and seeing that the items on the "to do" lists are addressed;

- sorting all new jobs into appropriate cells;

- adjusting labor standards to reflect lean improvements;

- coordinating the logistics and resources for each kaizen event;

- communicating to all production personnel the time and place of events or training, in addition to keeping everyone informed of improvement results;

- monitoring key daily metrics on cells;

- training supervisors, team leaders, and water spiders as needed;

- maintaining a training room and providing the necessary materials for training;

- overseeing skills training and maintaining a skills matrix for each worker;

- establishing cell teams with individuals responsible for 5S, quality, production improvements, etc.;

- participating on the kaizen suggestion team;

- providing a weekly report on kaizen activities to the director of continuous improvement;

- looking for ways to network with other plants and share events with vendors and customers; and

- preparing periodic formal presentations on the progress of kaizen implementation to management.

EVENT COORDINATOR'S ROLE

The event coordinator is the highest-ranking administrative clerk involved with the kaizen event. This person is the liaison between top management, the team leaders,

Event Coordinator Responsibilities

Safety

Monitor progress

Coaching

Diplomacy

Communication

Referee

and team members for all non-lean activities relating to the logistics of the event. He or she has the ultimate authority to make decisions concerning the event.

It is important for the event coordinator to keep abreast of the progress of each team on a daily basis to see that needs are being met. Logical break points to check on teams are at lunch and at the end of each day. Regular reporting times will keep the teams cognizant of the compressed schedule and the fact that there must be continued progress.

Additional responsibilities of the event coordinator include delegating assignments to the appropriate persons, safety at the event, clarifying policy issues with management, and approving expenditures for material needed to complete improvements. At times, the event coordinator will work with the plant accountant to determine the justification of a contemplated expenditure. In general, all behind-the-scenes activities not assigned to the team leaders fall upon the event coordinator.

Production Supervisor Meetings

Soon after the kaizen event begins, the event coordinator should meet with the production supervisors from the affected areas to find out how things are going. This is to address problems and determine if the production workers are getting along with the kaizen teams. Any negative comments should be addressed immediately. One common complaint of production workers not on the event is that they do not understand why all the changes are necessary nor do they see the purpose. The event coordinator should inform production workers as things are happening, not after.

Presentation of Results and Celebration

At the presentation of results, the event coordinator is responsible for inviting the appropriate audience and providing hard copies of each team's presentation to those who want them.

The logistics of the Friday wrap-up session are also the responsibility of the event coordinator. This includes arranging for the room, equipment, the celebration afterwards, awards and certificates, team pictures, and acting as master of ceremonies during the presentations.

The celebration serves two purposes: it celebrates the completion of an intense period of pressure and is a time to "show off." For the event coordinator, the celebration is the final event responsibility.

The celebration should be "team" focused and not "event" focused. Support people, such as the maintenance workers, forklift drivers, the person who ordered the food, and anyone else who was instrumental to the success of the event should be invited. Local dignitaries are also invited.

It is the event coordinator's responsibility to see that the event is given coverage in the company newspaper. Likewise, local newspaper coverage is also sought. The union should be involved in the celebration and the publicity.

MANAGEMENT'S ROLE

In collaboration with the lean consultant, management keeps a watchful eye on kaizen event implementation by reviewing progress reports and walking the plant floor on a regular basis. It is the ongoing responsibility of the company's leadership to outwardly show their commitment to the practice of kaizen. They must inspire cultural change and encourage continuous improvement efforts; they must "walk the walk" as well as "talk the talk."

At the kaizen event celebration, the plant manager and higher company officials should thank all involved and express their gratitude for the hard work and accomplishments of the teams. Management should address the recommendations and agree to following up on them. If there are reasons that follow-ups can not be completed, then the teams should be told why. In either instance, management should thank the teams for submitting the suggestions and offering the opportunity to act upon them. Comments should be made as to the teams' results and the next steps, possibly including a hint as to the location of the next event. The consultant and the company's lean champion also should add their overview of the week's results.

Other forms of recognition may include keepsakes for the team members. Hats, shirts, jackets or other items are walking advertisements of the kaizen event's success. Likewise, a certificate displaying the team's photo can be given to each team member as the plant manager shakes their hands.

Six

Preparing for a Kaizen Event

GUIDELINES FOR MANAGEMENT

This chapter contains suggestions based on real-life experiences with kaizen. It will help managers understand and identify specific tasks that must be completed, or at least considered, prior to conducting a kaizen event.

Much of the success of a kaizen event is determined by the thoroughness of the planning. Many tasks must be coordinated and accomplished before the event begins, because once the event is underway, it will be too late to go back and do them. Nevertheless, plans are only good if they can be implemented. "Urgency" is the key word. It is better to do something quickly and make adjustments later than to make the perfect plan and not be able to implement it. Likewise, it is better to learn by doing rather than trying to second guess by planning the perfect solution. After all, only if gains are sustained do plans succeed.

Many variables are present with each event, and there is the possibility of problems arising at any stage. However, with proper foresight and planning, most problems are avoidable.

The first step in planning a kaizen event is to review the last one held and make adjustments as needed. A study of the team leader's suggestions for improvement as well as the post-event questionnaires is recommended. What did the participants say? Kaizen events, like any other process, will get better when "kaizened." Results will get easier to achieve too.

Consultant's Role

At companies where there is no experience with kaizen, the first few kaizen events should be professionally conducted by a consultant. Chances should not be taken by trying to do them without expertise. Success with kaizen is too important. There is too much at stake. A company may decide to conduct further kaizen events on its own once there have been several successes and people have been adequately trained.

For the first event, a consultant may handle one or two teams. More teams may be handled by the consultant once team members gain confidence, and if the team leaders are competent in leading the teams. Later on, team leaders will replace the consultant and the consultant need only monitor the events, not lead them. Each event becomes easier to conduct and the results increasingly more predictable. The real test lies in the ability of teams to teach others what the Toyota Production System (TPS) and kaizen are all about.

Kaizen and Workforce Reduction

Management's intent of kaizen implementation should never be to reduce the workforce by layoffs. It should be made perfectly clear to everyone that they will not lose their jobs as a result of the improvements the teams will make. Workers might be reassigned or end up on a kaizen team that will go around the plant conducting events, but no one should fear for their livelihood. Displaced workers can be reassigned to work brought back in, to replace temporary workers, or to work on prototypes or process development. Or, they may receive additional training so they may be reassigned to a total productive maintenance (TPM) team or become a trainer.

As a result of kaizen, team members will have more involvement, more excitement, and more chances to make real decisions about their jobs. Morale will be definitely improved.

Human Resources

The Human Resources (HR) department needs to get involved at the very beginning. There needs to be a weeding-out process to ensure that, as teams are selected, there will be no "cement heads"—those who do not want to cooperate or who feel kaizen will not work. These negative thinkers should not be assigned to a team.

Human Resources also should do some training prior to starting the kaizen events. Since kaizen will be new to most of the workforce, the subject of "change management" is appropriate. This educates people on what to expect in the workplace as a result of change, and how to deal with it in a personal way. Another subject that can be addressed is "participative management"—the principle on which kaizen was founded and the key to the success of the Toyota Production System. Participative management encourages decisions to be made at the low-

est level of the organization, by the people most directly affected. The most difficult aspect of change may be the acceptance of workers to now be allowed to make improvements.

Unions

Unions are intended to protect workers. They prevent unfairness, promote seniority, and represent workers as a single voice to the company. Unions are concerned with the workers' benefits and welfare. In essence, they *are* the workers.

Kaizen *reinforces* the security of workers' jobs by not allowing layoffs. It promotes training, recognition, and fairness—all goals of unions. When looked at in depth, kaizen brings to a worker and his future the exact objectives that unions hold foremost. Kaizen is "union friendly."

The support of union executives is vital to the success of kaizen. To prepare for kaizen, management should make sure union executives are included in as many preliminary decisions and policy meetings as possible.

Provisions should be added to the union contract mandating the company's adoption of the Toyota

Production System. Everyone should be made aware that the union is an integral part of the strategic plan to implement TPS. The company and the union representing the workers are partners. So the union should be allowed to have a representative in the kaizen support office or on the core team.

Communication

Communication begins at the top and eventually migrates to everyone. Keeping everyone informed of kaizen helps dispel fear of the unknown. Everyone should be kept abreast of what is happening on a daily basis if possible. This is key to building and maintaining trust with the workforce. Good communication dispels rumors.

When the details of a kaizen event are known, they should be published. Line operators and all personnel scheduled to be on a kaizen team must be informed, interviewed, and ready to actively participate. No one should be left uninformed. Education includes attending training on "Participative Management" and "Change Management" before the event.

A kaizen event will affect many workers in the plant, not just those on the teams. Management must be sure personnel can support the event as well as maintain regular production. Outside resources should be called in if needed.

If possible, communication to the workforce should flow through the union by letter or other medium.

The union should be totally involved in spreading the message. This builds trust in the union and the company. It should be made apparent that this is a team effort.

Goals and Objectives

Prior to the actual kaizen event, the descriptions and methodology of the kaizen should be posted for everyone in the plant to see. The posting explains the area to be affected and the expected benefits of changes. Goals and objectives are clearly outlined. Workers should be asked to keep an open mind to the benefits of the changes. The overall plan should describe how everyone will be included in the training and implementation.

If there is a company newsletter, pictures of the areas before and after should be published. A picture is worth a thousand words. Also of interest are pictures of the team members at work during the kaizen event. For example, management and union personnel could be shown working alongside operators. This will promote the team concept and reiterate that people have no rank for kaizen events. All are considered equal and everyone is a team player.

It is recommended to automatically include maintenance and support workers in all events. As part of the team, they should be invited to enjoy a free lunch alongside everyone else as they are working on event projects. And they should always be invited to the Friday presentations so they can share in the recognition.

Selecting the Kaizen Area

In selecting an area for the first kaizen event, multiple-model lines should not be considered. They should be saved for later when teams are more experienced. In addition, if choosing a complicated manufacturing line, it must be able to be broken into small cells. The first kaizen area should be a production line where:

- The line is guaranteed to succeed.

- A complete product is produced—not a process.

- The line is visual.

- Improvements can be copied and used in other areas.

- Changes to the line make a significant, positive impact on a bottleneck or production restriction.

- Improvements will have a significant market or financial impact.

- Operational problems are evident—not management or policy issues.

- There is a sound initial process.

- There is a product that can be made in a cell, needing not more than 12 operators.

- A product is produced in medium-to-high volume.

- Most employees are familiar with the line.

- Everything is a disaster—the worst area in the plant (for effect).

- The product must go through four to six processes to complete a part.

- Production can be broken into small manageable cells.

- The line wanders all over the plant.

- The line is buried with work-in-process (WIP).

- People will most likely respond favorably, for example, on a line with operators who have been cross-trained and exposed to other kaizen events.

- The area was shown as a "starburst" on the current-state value stream map.

- There is relatively good overall equipment effectiveness (OEE).

Each new event is a training ground for new team leaders. And, each new event becomes easier than the last because of the experience gained.

Several site choices should be made so each can be compared and ranked in a matrix. This process will help determine where subsequent events will be held. The first area is chosen so that what is learned there can be applied to the next. The idea is to start easy and slow and progress to more challenging areas as the team gains confidence and experience.

Selecting Team Members

In selecting a team, the following criteria should be considered:

- At least half of the team members should be chosen from outside the event area (sales and marketing, engineering, maintenance, production control, front office, warehouse, management, sister plants, etc.).

- The makeup of the team should be one-third operators, one-third kaizen support, and one-third personnel from other areas.

- The team should consist of 6–12 members, with the ideal size being 7–8.

- At least two operators should be from the event area.

- The team leader must have previous event experience as a co-leader or team leader.

- The co-leader must have taken part in a kaizen event before.

- Ask for volunteers.

- Complete outsiders, vendors or customers, or people from other plants or even other companies can add diversity and perspective to the team.

- The persons chosen should be outwardly creative.

- Union executives should be included.

- Maintenance people should be included, if available.

Selecting Team Leaders

The choice of a team leader can mean the crucial difference between success and tremendous success of an event. Rookies, those who are domineering, complainers, and critics do not make good team leaders. The team leader should not be from the event area. The more removed from the area the better. This way there will not be any cries of favoritism.

Management should notify the team leader of his or her assignment well in advance of the event so sched-

ules can be adjusted. The reasons for selecting the area also should be explained to the leader beforehand. Most importantly, it should be made clear that the event takes priority over any other work assignment.

The primary responsibilities of a team leader are to keep the team on track and meet the objectives of the event. A team leader does not need to have the answers as to how and what will be improved. The answers to all the problems will come from within the team. What he or she does need are people skills, specifically to know how to get people to open up.

The same criteria as above apply to selecting a co-leader for the team.

Traits of Team Leaders

Team leaders should possess the following traits:

- experience and success in leadership, but not necessarily management (for example, a scoutmaster or soldier);

- experience as a co-leader on previous kaizen events;

- exposure to the tools of the Toyota Production System (TPS);

- familiarity with the parts and process of the kaizen event area (homework may be necessary);

- an explicit understanding of what the words *urgent*, *discipline*, and *teamwork* mean;

- a management style that is not dictatorial;

- an understanding that the shop floor is where they need to be— a team leader can not lead a team from an office;

- an understanding of participative management theory; and

- must be friendly but aggressive, firm but fair, but in control when necessary.

Preparing for the Kaizen Event

Equipment and Materials

Earlier in this chapter it was mentioned that preparation was the make-it or break-it activity that absolutely had to be right. Even with proper preparation, if the materials and equipment are not there, a successful kaizen event becomes nearly impossible. The check sheet shown in Figure 6-1 can be used to plan and organize material and equipment needs for a kaizen event.

Typical equipment required for a kaizen event may include:

- hand tools;

- hammers;

- duct tape;

- cardboard;

- wood and nails;

- masking tape;

- floor marking tape;

- tape measures;

- chalk lines;

- quick-change hookups for utilities (air, electrical, water, and coolant);

- sufficient connectors to link up the utilities (hoses, pipes, extension cords, etc.);

Material and Equipment Checklist

Event date _____   Area _____   Event coordinator _____

Item #	Materials and Equipment	Description	Quantity on Hand	Quantity to Buy	Total Quantity	Date Needed	Total Cost	Procured by Whom
1	Hand tools	Hammers						
		Tape measures						
		Chalk lines						
		Duct tape						
		Cardboard						
		Wood and nails						
		Floor marking tape						
2	Utility hookups	Air						
		Electrical						
		Water						
		Coolant						
		Other						
3	Cleaning supplies	Mops						
		Brooms						
		Buckets						
		Degreasers						
		Soap						
		Paint thinner						
		Sprayers						
		Rags						
4	Video equipment	Video camera						
		Digital camera						
		Monitors						
		Software						
5	Handcarts	Hand tools						
6	Forklifts	With team driver						
7	Flip charts, markers	Pads						
		Pencils						
		Easles						
		Markers						
8	Safety equipment	Shoes						
		Glasses						
		Hats						
		Other						
9	Stopwatches	1 for every 2 people						
10	Break-out rooms	For each team						

Figure 6-1.

- handcarts to contain the tools and allow for movement around the area;

- forklifts with team members able to drive them;

- flip charts, markers, whiteboards, and clipboards;

- safety equipment (safety glasses, shoes, hats, special clothing, etc.);

- stopwatches—at least one for every two people;

- Break-out rooms on the shop floor;

- cleaning supplies (mops, buckets, degreasers, paint, brushes, solvent for paint thinning and clean-up, sprayers, rags, rags, and more rags!); and

- video cameras, monitors, and computers with software to allow digital reproduction of the pictures for the report-out presentation.

One last item to note is that plant security should be notified of what will be going on so they do not panic when they see people doing things never seen before, at all hours of the day and night!

Preparing the Area

The selected area should be fairly uncluttered, so there is no need to spend the bulk of the time removing unnecessary junk. Time is better spent on implementing change, not uncovering the existing mess. An exception would be a 5S (simplify; set in order; scrub and shine; stabilize and standardize; sustain) event, where the task is to completely clean and organize an area. (Sometimes it is a good idea to have a 5S event before a cell designing event to maximize results.)

Consideration should be paid to the effect the event will have upstream and downstream from the target area. The following questions should be asked.

- Will this move a bottleneck to another area? Or will it eliminate a lot of bad situations?

- Does there need to be stock built up and, if so, where and how much?

- In case production must be run, what are the requirements?

- How will the event affect other shifts? Will the other shifts understand what was done and why? Each shift should be represented during the event if possible.

Support Personnel

Some companies hire outside contractors to assist with factory maintenance during a kaizen event. This frees the company's support personnel so they can work on event-related items. It is important that the rest of the plant continue to be productive while the event is going on.

To make coordination of the kaizen support activities easier, specific maintenance personnel should be assigned to work with each team and a liaison from each team appointed to work with the maintenance people. A liaison is necessary so multiple members of the kaizen team are not redirecting the maintenance team with differing instructions. This allows for consistency in setting priorities and prevents confusion.

On the first day there is usually no need for maintenance in the morning since training is taking place. Occasionally a team gets ambitious and there is a need for maintenance to start moving machines the first night, but generally not. The second day is usually when the need to move machines and equipment arises in earnest, especially after noon and into the night, and sometimes well into the early morning.

Like soldiers in uniforms, or a sports team ready for the big game, team members, as well as support personnel, should be identifiable. This may be accomplished by wearing special shirts or hats. Everyone in the plant should be able to identify the team and see the activities as they are happening.

It is prudent for maintenance personnel to anticipate the items that require purchase before the event. They should make sure the needed items are on hand so time is not wasted by having to go out and buy them at the last minute. It is also a good idea for maintenance personnel to keep a record of the typical items and tasks needed for an event. This will help with new events, making it easier to anticipate needs, and saving a lot of time.

Background Information

Critical background information must be investigated before the kaizen event takes place. At many events, a lot of time is wasted looking for the data and production information necessary to make decisions on parameters such as takt time, product mix, and process requirements. To alleviate having to search for missing information at the last minute, the following are tips on what to compile:

- parts quantity analysis and flow charts;

- current process and operation sheets;

- customer production requirements by the week, month, and day, along with Pareto charts of each;

- model mix information;

- up-to-date layouts of each area affected, large enough to hang on a wall, and reproductions on 8-1/2 × 11 paper for team members to carry with them to the shop floor; and

- a roster of operators, including specific job descriptions.

Team Preparation

Since it is assumed that team leaders have had previous experience as co-leaders or as members of a kaizen team, it should not be necessary to explain in detail what is expected of them. It is necessary, however, to review with them the facts specific to the event:

- event location;

- team members;

- production requirements;

- goals and objectives;

- plant rules, including safety guidelines (smoking, leaving plant property, tornado warnings, etc.);

- team member expectations;

- handling roadblocks and personality conflicts;

- typical gains from previous events;

- past problems encountered; and

- who will be at the report-out presentation and why (include the owners and sponsors who need to sustain the gains once implemented).

In regard to the event, the team leader is responsible for the following:

- gathering the necessary information, including layouts, flow charts, cycle time charts, and takt time charts, process sheets, etc.;

- organizing activities and communicating the event objectives and goals, including staffing and savings calculations;

- monitoring what everyone is doing;

- charting takt and cycle times;

- coordinating the preparation of the final presentation;

- compiling a hard copy of the presentation and distributing it to management and others;

- completing all the items on the follow-up list; and

- acting as liaison to the next team leader to communicate the outcome of the event.

Each team should be given a kit containing supplies that will be needed to write, draw, sketch, tape, and illustrate the ideas and concepts. It should contain all the necessary paper, pens, pencils, erasers, sticky notes, markers, stopwatches, etc. (see Figure 6-1 for a checklist).

Videos or digital pictures of the areas should be taken before the event so that after improvements are made there can be visual comparisons. A digital camera can be used instead of a video camera if preferred. The digital pictures can be presented on overheads or with an LCD projector. Usually the team leader will assign the photography task to someone on the team. The team leader should review the "before" videos and photos with the team to familiarize them with the situation and area. As the team progresses, the "work in progress" should continue to be digitally documented. This makes for an interesting presentation story. However, video should not replace the actual time studies that will need to be conducted for each worker by the team.

Logistics

During the event, team members will be required to participate 100% without interruption. This means no cellular calls and no running back and forth between their "regular" jobs and the event.

All of the needs of the team should be automatically met. Flip charts, whiteboards, markers and all of the items from the kit should be made available in the breakout rooms. There should be monitors and computers available too.

Breakout rooms for each team should be quiet and private, without interruptions (no plant-wide intercoms). There should be refreshments readily available, as well as restroom facilities. To save time and maintain continuity, it is recom-

mended that the plant provide meals and refreshments for the teams for the duration of the event. Accommodation should be given to special dietary needs.

Though breakout rooms are provided, the majority of time will be spent out on the shop floor where production takes place. The shop floor is where good things happen. Kaizen is about doing. Doing something first, then analyzing it, then doing it again, only better. Learning comes from doing. Thus the amount of time spent in the breakout rooms should be minimal. Time spent there should be limited to the planning sessions or to time-out or rest breaks. Later on, the breakout room is where the presentation will be put together.

Visitors

Cross-functional teams, which include people from different areas of business, tend to make the best teams. So team members from out of town are frequently assigned. When they are, attention should be paid to the arrangements that will be necessary to accommodate them.

Flights or other transportation must be arranged in advance and guarantee arrival before the event begins. Hotel reservations must be made in advance, as well as arrangements for transportation to and from the hotel to the plant if rental cars are not used. Usually most people arrive on Monday morning for the event. However, if long travel times and distances are involved, they should arrive the night before.

In the case of team leaders who are considered "visitors," they should be available either the day before the event or early on Monday morning to review the goals and objectives and get a feel for the area. Most of the data will have been provided to them prior to the event, so that they may review it and plan their strategy.

Team Celebration

Though a kaizen event is hard work, it also can be fun. In planning for the event, there are two possibilities for team recognition and celebration. The first is to have an introduction dinner for all the team members early in the week on Tuesday or Wednesday. This allows the teams time to get to know one another. The second is to plan a luncheon on Friday after the report-out presentations. An advantage of the introduction dinner over the Friday luncheon is that after the presentations on Friday, team members are free to leave, making it a short day. The decision depends on what suits the plant and the personnel involved. Regardless of the timing, it is never a good idea to include alcoholic beverages at the celebration.

The phrase, "five days and one night" is often used to describe the length of a kaizen event. This comes from the fact that usually there is at least one long work night. Sometimes teams get so involved in making changes that they do not want to stop for a planned dinner. They need the time to complete their improvements (such dedication!). Other times teams will work late and order pizza for later. In any case, accommodations should be made to keep the momentum going.

Figure 6-2 is a checklist for shop-floor kaizen event preparation.

Shop-floor Kaizen Event Preparation Checklist

Event Date _____ Area _____ Event coordinator_____

#	Activity	Description	Done	To Do	Amount	When	By Whom
1	Overall event	Develop goals and objectives for teams					
		Verify against strategic plan					
		Solicit input from staff on area criteria					
		Select team leaders					
		Select teams					
		Communications to parties concerned					
		Accommodations					
2	Logistics	Caterer selected and menus chosen for lunches, dinners, breakfast and breaks					
		Hotel accommodations for visitors					
		Transportation for visitors					
		Guest invitations for presentation					
		Breakout rooms reserved					
		Tables and chairs, flip charts, etc.					
		Data for teams					
		Main conference/training room reserved					
		Awards purchased and certificates printed					
3	Shop-floor activities	Production coverage provided					
		Support personnel contacted					
		Special equipment or support arranged					
		Maintenance materials sufficient					
		Cleaning and painting materials on hand					
		Safety equipment working and sufficient					
4	Team supplies	Materials and equipment checklist fulfilled					
		Cameras, video cams, monitors reserved					
		Software available					
		LCDs available					
5	Training sessions	Training rooms reserved					
		Extra flip charts and markers					
		Overhead projector and LCD available					
6	Communications	Corporate					
		Shop floor					
		Union					
7	Finance and support personnel	Controller notified					
		Production control notified					
		Manufacturing engineers available					
		CAD/CAM equipment available					
8	Community involvement	Local newspaper notified					
		Local radio and television notified					
		Company newsletter notified					
		Presentation speech written					

Figure 6-2.

Seven
How to Lead a Team During the Event

TEAM LEADER

Responsible for making dramatic changes within inflexible time constraints, the team leader is truly on the front line, in the midst of battle. A mediator and mentor, a motivator and critic, at times the team leader has to behave like a general, and at others like a best friend. Thus the team leader must be democratic in style while insisting on constantly pursuing the kaizen event's objectives. He or she must blend the eagerness of the team with the concerns of the operators to achieve the desired results.

The team leader guides the team, encouraging creative ideas and experimentation while focusing on real-time, practical solutions. Fear of failure can inhibit creativity. However, shotgun approaches usually lead to total loss of direction and focus, as well as bringing higher levels of stress and never achieving success. There must be a balance—the degree of risk must be weighted against the safety of maintaining status quo.

It is the job of the team leader to seek out viable ideas that will produce tangible results, giving team members and sponsors a feeling of accomplishment. Implementation counts for everything and the team should not be afraid to take credit for ideas that have been around a long time but never acted on. It is ultimately better to fully reach a few objectives than to have partial and incomplete progress in many.

The elimination of waste starts with how the team leader leads the team. Time should not be wasted on trivial issues or personal agendas. Nevertheless, a kaizen event should be "fun" for everyone. The team leader should remember to pause frequently to assess the situation and ask, "are we having fun yet?" This chapter describes in detail how to make the event a fun, rewarding experience for everyone involved.

TEAM ORIENTATION

First thing on Monday, the team members are introduced to one another. Each member is asked to tell a little something about themselves: name, company, how long with the company, job function, hobbies or activities when not at work, and knowledge and experience with kaizen events.

The team leader covers the logistical information: the location of restrooms, break times, lunch plans, and what to do in case of an emergency. It is good to remind everyone that cell phones are to be turned off or put in silent mode. It is expected that a team member's commitment to the event means uninterrupted attention to daily activities.

Everyone is reminded of team member responsibilities: the team leader is responsible to keep the event on track, monitor team member contributions, and keep an eye on the clock to ensure adherence to the schedule. If some team members are reluctant to participate, the team leader offers words of encouragement and reminds everyone that all team members carry the same rank.

Toyota Production System (TPS) Training

Usually, the consultant conducts the first few kaizen events at a company. He or she may conduct a special training session for team leaders. It is recommended that all aspiring team leaders attend this preliminary session since they will be responsible for team training in the future.

The entire kaizen team is required to attend and actively participate in TPS training on Monday. If needed, a half-day Tuesday can be added. Occasionally, an auditor may monitor the class for reasons that might not be clear to the team leader or rest of the team. These "auditors" should be quiet and inconspicuous during training as they are not part of the team. Chapter 2 of this manual details the specifics of TPS training.

When people are attending TPS training for the second or third time, they should be asked to co-lead the team and/or assist the team leader in some way. This allows them a greater chance for participation in recognition of their TPS knowledge, and gives them experience so they can advance to being a team leader in the future. There is enough work for everyone!

TEAM PACKAGE

The team leader's responsibilities are reviewed with the team and a package of materials is distributed to each member before the event starts. The package includes the following information:

- plant layout and event area layout,
- flow chart and process sheet,
- cycle time of current process,
- customer requirements or takt time,
- staff and support personnel list,
- scrap and rework data/production model mix,

- average number of changeovers per day and times,
- goals and objectives of the event,
- list of current problems,
- improvement projects currently being considered,
- safety issues/company/union rules, and
- the week's agenda and a daily agenda. See Figure 7-1 for a typical kaizen event schedule.

During the event it is recommended that the team leader to meet with the team members to coordinate activities and compare results at least twice daily. The team leader should make the times known to the team. This will help keep the team focused on results.

10 Rules for a Kaizen Event

The 10 rules of a kaizen event are posted in plain view for everyone to see. They are reviewed by the team and briefly discussed so everyone has a common mindset as the event begins. The 10 rules are as follows:

1. There is no rank among team members (one person, one vote).

Kaizen Event Schedule

Monday

8:00 a.m.—Orientation

9:00 a.m.—Toyota Production System (TPS) training begins

8:00 p.m.—First day of TPS training ends

Tuesday

7:00 a.m.—TPS training continues

12:00 p.m.—TPS training complete

1:00 p.m.—Team begins to document the current state

? p.m.—Current state data collection completed, team leader meeting

Wednesday

7:00 a.m.—Future state development begins

12:00 p.m.—Future State Mapping Checklist and New Process Requirements Checklist completed

? p.m.—Design of the new process completed, team leader meeting

Thursday

7:00 a.m.—Review of physical changes made by maintenance

9:30 a.m.—Operators try new process, time study

2:30 p.m.— All work complete, begin report-outs

? p.m.—Report-outs completed, management walks the site to review improvements

Friday

7:00 a.m.—Presentation rehearsals

9:00 a.m.—Presentations begin

12:00 p.m.—Event ends, celebration begins

Figure 7-1.

2. Keep an open mind to change.

3. Change is good; more change is better.

4. Maintain a positive attitude.

5. Nobody blames anyone for anything.

6. Respect each other.

7. There is no such thing as a dumb question.

8. Plans are only good if they can be implemented.

9. Plans succeed only if the gains are sustained.

10. There is no substitute for hard work.

STEP 1: CURRENT STATE MAPPING

One common difficulty encountered is that after TPS training on the first two days, the team wants to jump right in and fix things. Showing enthusiasm, people want to bypass the data collection and analysis tasks, which are critically important to the success of improvements. The team leader cannot allow the team to skip this all-important step. The exercise of gathering the data forces the team to dig deep into the operation and really get a feel for the process. It is usually a real eye-opener.

The team leader begins the current state mapping process by using the product routing checklist shown in Figure 7-2 to guide the team. A Standard Work Sheet, such as the one shown in Figure 7-3, is used to organize the data. Following are instructions for completing the Standard Work Sheet.

1. Scope of operations: fill in the first and last tasks of the production process.

2. Draw a diagram of the physical layout of the cell area as defined by the position of the machines used in the production sequence.

3. Order of operations: number all of the operations on the machine layout diagram in the order of the production process and connect the operations to indicate the direction of the process flow. Use a solid line to indicate connections that occur in all cases and a dotted line for alternate routings.

4. Standard work-in-process (WIP): this is the unavoidable

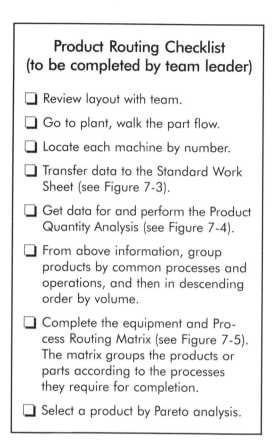

Product Routing Checklist
(to be completed by team leader)

❏ Review layout with team.

❏ Go to plant, walk the part flow.

❏ Locate each machine by number.

❏ Transfer data to the Standard Work Sheet (see Figure 7-3).

❏ Get data for and perform the Product Quantity Analysis (see Figure 7-4).

❏ From above information, group products by common processes and operations, and then in descending order by volume.

❏ Complete the equipment and Process Routing Matrix (see Figure 7-5). The matrix groups the products or parts according to the processes they require for completion.

❏ Select a product by Pareto analysis.

Figure 7-2.

WIP needed when work proceeds in the proper sequence. Note the inventory at the machines where it is needed and indicate the amount.

5. Indicate the total standard WIP for the cell in the labeled box.

6. Quality checks: draw a ◇ at each machine where a quality

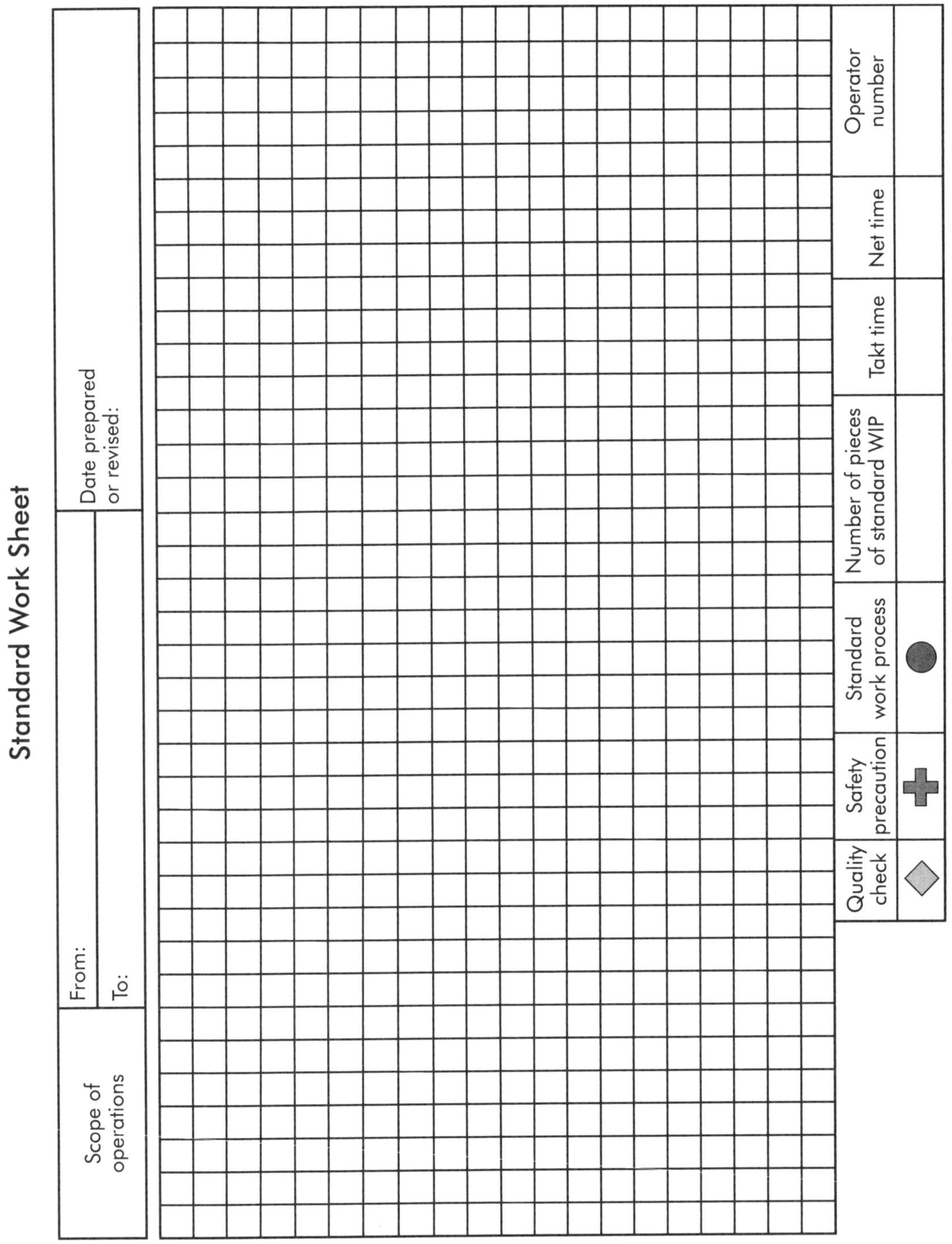

Standard Work Sheet

Scope of operations	From:		Date prepared or revised:
	To:		

Quality check ◇	Safety precaution ✚	Standard work process ●	Number of pieces of standard WIP	Takt time	Net time	Operator number

Figure 7-3.

Kaizen Event Implementation Manual

check is listed in the current process.

7. Safety precautions: draw a ✚ at each machine where special safety precautions are required.

8. Takt time: place the calculated takt time in the space provided.

9. Cycle time: fill in the operator's cycle time when tasks proceed according to the established order of operations.

A Product Quantity Analysis Matrix, such as the one shown in Figure 7-4, is completed to determine product families using common downstream process steps and equipment. Knowing these interrelationships on a macro level will help to position equipment or locations to achieve a minimum of handling and transportation. Figure 7-5 shows an example of an Equipment and Process Routing Matrix. This matrix is used to examine process routing on a micro level to determine where improvements can be made.

Product Quantity Analysis Matrix									
		Process Steps and Equipment							
Product	Quantity	1	2	3	4	5	6	7	8
A	200	X	X	X		X	X		
B	150	X	X	X	X	X	X		
C	200	X	X	X		X	X	X	
D	30		X	X	X		X	X	
E	120		X	X	X			X	X
F	100	X		X		X	X		
G	80	X		X		X	X	X	
H	100	X		X		X	X	X	

Figure 7-4.

Equipment and Process Routing Matrix											
		1	2	3	4	5	6	7	8	9	10
Station	Quantity	Small Hand Tools	Medium Hand Tools	Large Hand Tools	Electric Powered Tools	Electric Powered Special Tools	Electronic Specialty Tools	OEM Tools	Export & Licensee Tooling	Low Volume Special Equipment	Replacement Parts
Stamping & Forging	200	X	X	X	X	X	X	X		X	X
Assembly Area 1	300	X	X	X	X	X		X			
Assembly Area 2	150				X	X	X				
Assembly Area 3	20									X	
Final Assembly	300	X	X	X	X						
Heavy Machining	600	X	X	X	X	X	X	X	X	X	X
Heat Treat	320	X	X	X	X	X		X	X	X	X
Plating	150	X	X	X	X	X		X	X	X	X
Grinding	270	X	X	X	X	X		X	X	X	X
Electronic Assembly	50						X				
Packing & Shipping	600	X	X	X	X	X	X	X	X	X	X
Painting	250			X	X	X	X	X	X	X	
Welding	220	X	X	X	X	X		X	X	X	X

Identical processes   Similar processes

Figure 7-5.

The current situation must be thoroughly understood before improvements are made. It is important to have complete data available for the team so that no time is wasted looking for it. It is also extremely important that the data be correct. It is worse to have corrupted and suspect data than to have none at all.

The current process mapping checklist shown in Figure 7-6 will guide the team in completing the current state map.

Current Process Mapping Checklist (to be completed by team leader)

❑ Complete the Standard Work Sheet (see Figure 7-3).

❑ Route products and measure travel distance.

❑ Calculate square footage occupied by the current process.

❑ Count all work in process (WIP).

❑ Count current staffing.

❑ Determine all support persons assigned to the area.

❑ Investigate changeovers and their frequency.

❑ Investigate the current scrap rate and where it comes from.

❑ Determine bottlenecks and their reason.

Figure 7-6.

5S Survey

Some teams choose to do a 5S survey at this step. The form in Figure 7-7 can be used to evaluate the area. The survey is usually performed by a third-party observer or the plant manager. The results of the survey can point the team to where improvements can be made in the new process.

Collecting Time Data

When the product and process routings are completed and the appropriate forms filled out, the next task is to collect the time study data for the process. Using the checklist in Figure 7-8, the team leader guides the team in collecting the data. A Time Observation Sheet, such as the one shown in Figure 7-9, is completed for each operator. Instructions for completing this sheet are as follows.

1. Measure manual work times, machine cycle times, and operator walking times within the operation.

    a. Observe the operation two or three times to be sure of the sequence of operations, order of each task, work methods being used, and to determine the component tasks.

#	Task Description	5S Evaluation & Scoring Criteria 5 = Excellent 0 = Poor	Score	Improvement Comments
1	Removal of unnecessary items	All unnecessary items not associated with the job are removed; only work tools and products are present.		
2	Storage of cleaning materials	Cleaning materials are stored in a neat manner; handy and easily accessible, in good condition.		
3	Floor cleaning	All floors are clean and free of debris, oil, grease, and obvious dirt and grime. Cleaning is done daily.		
4	Bulletin boards	All material is up to date; Standard Work Combination Sheets are posted and in use. Safety notices are included.		
5	Emergency access	Safety and fire equipment are unobstructed and accessible. Switches and emergency stops are functional and identified in red.		
6	Items on floor	Tools, WIP, empty bins, etc., are not left on floor. Items on floor are assigned to parking spaces and in correct places.		
7	Aisle markings	Aisles and walkways are clearly marked; parking spaces are clearly marked and at right angles to aisles.		
8	Aisle maintenance	Aisles are not used for staging WIP or obstructed by boxes or pallets; not slippery and wet. They are well lit.		
9	Storage and arrangement	Items in boxes or bins are not stacked so they lean or in a crooked stack. Storage is done only in designated areas.		
10	Equipment paint	All machines and equipment are painted and kept fresh looking. Everything 6 ft and lower is painted regularly.		
11	Equipment cleanliness	Machines and equipment are kept spotless by the operator.		
12	Equipment maintenance	Controls are clearly labeled. Critical points are checked daily by the operator; minor adjustments are made as needed.		
13	Equipment storage	Nothing is placed on top of machines, cabinets, or equipment. All guards and safety features are operational.		
14	Document storage	Only documents necessary to the work area and process are visible and up to date. They are stored in a neat manner.		
15	Document control	All documents are properly labeled and up to date. Documents are stored in numerical sequence.		
16	Tool and gage arrangement	Tools, jigs, fixtures, and raw materials are stored in a safe, easy-to-use place, and clearly labeled.		
17	Tooling accessibility	Tools are stored to facilitate quick changeovers. All gages are available.		
18	Location of shelves, benches, and desks	All are free of junk piled on them. There is not hidden junk inside cabinets. Everything is properly labeled.		
19	Use of shelves, benches, and desks	All shelves, benches, and desks are used for their proper purpose.		
20	5S control and maintenance	There is a disciplined system in place and regular inspections take place. There is follow-up on low scoring areas.		
		Total		(÷ 20 for average)

Figure 7-7.

**Time-data Collection Checklist
(to be completed by team leader)**

❑ Talk to the operators prior to doing time studies. Discuss the intent of the kaizen on their line.

❑ Time study each operator and record results on the Time Observation Sheet (see Figure 7-9).

❑ Calculate the takt time.

❑ Complete the Process Design Analysis Sheet (see Figure 7-11).

❑ Calculate the theoretical lead time.

❑ Document any unique processes or handling required.

❑ Determine the changeover frequency and times.

❑ Construct a spaghetti diagram.

Figure 7-8.

b. Enter the list of component tasks onto the Time Observation Sheet and, while watching the operation, remember each *observation point*. An observation point is the instant at which the end of an operation is read off a stopwatch. Observations can be made of component tasks of two or three seconds in duration.

c. Measure time.

• Without stopping the stopwatch, take a time reading at the end of each of the component tasks and enter the time on the top half of the appropriate row on the Time Observation Sheet.

• Observations must be repeated roughly 10 times.

• Note any exceptional tasks, abnormalities, or other points observed.

d. Calculate the individual component task times.

• Subtract the ending time of the previous operation from the current one to find the individual component task time duration.

• In red ink, enter the component task time in the lower half of that task's row.

e. Calculate the demonstrated time per cycle.

• Sum the individual component task times for each operational cycle and place the totals at the

Time Observation Sheet

Process:		Date:			Time:		Observer:		Checker:

No.	Component Tasks	Work Cycles 1 2 3 4 5 6 7 8 9 10 11 12 13 14 15	Total Time	Task Time Average	Points Observed

Time for one cycle

Lowest Repeatable Cycle Time Average

Figure 7-9.

bottom of each column in the space provided.

• Choose the best time value of the 10 or so observations and use this as the baseline.

f. Determine the time to be used for each of the component tasks.

• Calculate the average component task time and place it in the column labeled for it on the right side of the sheet.

• Be sure the total of the individual task times does not exceed the time used in step "e." (Do not change the cycle time.)

2. Find machine times.

a. Measure the time between each instance the "on" button is pressed and the point at which the machine returns to its original position after completing the target operation. Note this time on the Time Observation Sheet at the end of the same row where the machine start activity is

listed under the heading of "Points Observed." This is the machine cycle time (MCT).

b. Two or three observations of machine time should be sufficient as long as the machine cycles automatically. More observations will be required if the operator is integral to the machine cycle.

In addition, and before any improvements are made, the area should be videotaped and the process completely documented.

Cycle Time and Takt Time

The lowest repeatable cycle time is used as the base time for one operator during a time study. The importance of first getting all the elements of a process, and then the individual times should be stressed. The times are very important, as they will be used to do the line balancing.

A simple graph like the one in Figure 7-10 can be used to show the original cycle times from station to station. Existing process sheets or standards should not be used because most are inaccurate. The time

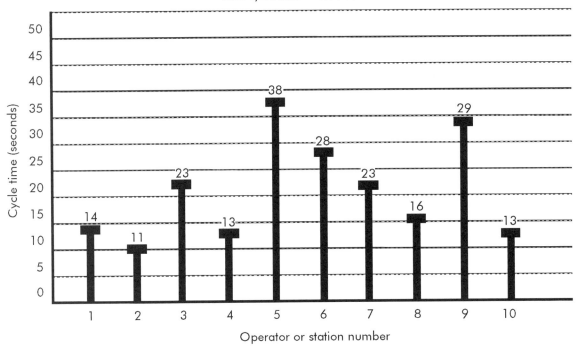

Figure 7-10.

study must be conducted with each operator at each workstation to be certain of the cycle times. Actual times can then be used as "real" standards.

Takt time is the pulse of the factory—the beat at which parts must be produced to satisfy the customers' demand. To calculate takt time,

$$T_t = \frac{T_o}{T_q}$$ (Eq. 7-1)

where:

T_t = takt time
T_o = total daily operating time
T_q = total daily quantity required

So, if shift time = 8 hours = 28,800 seconds and there is a requirement of 1,000 pieces/shift minus two breaks at 10 minutes (600 seconds) each,

$$28,800 - 1,200 = 27,600$$

$$T_t = \frac{T_o}{T_q} = \frac{27,600}{1,000}$$

T_t = 27.6 seconds per piece

To calculate the number of operators required,

$$O_n = \frac{C_t}{T_t} \qquad \text{(Eq. 7-2)}$$

where:

O_n = number of operators
C_t = total of all cycle times
T_t = takt time

So, using the total of the cycle times charted in Figure 7-10 and the takt time derived from Eq. 7-1,

$$O_n = \frac{C_t}{T_t} = \frac{208}{27.6}$$
$$= 7.5 \text{ operators or}$$
$$\text{stations required}$$

The number is rounded up to eight operators until non-value added activities can be eliminated.

Process Analysis

Once the time data is collected, a Process Design Analysis Sheet, such as the one shown in Figure 7-11, is filled in. The Value-adding Determination shown in Figure 7-12 will be needed to complete the Process Design Analysis Sheet.

A Process Capacity Table, such as the one in Figure 7-13, is also required. Following are instructions for its completion.

1. Step no.: numbers entered in this column should match the process sequence numbers assigned to each machine.

2. Process description: fill in the process names for each operator/machine/part combination.

   a. Fill in each machine name separately when there are two or more machines in a single process.

   b. Note if a single machine processes two or more parts per cycle.

   c. Note periodic operations, such as chip removal, quality checks, tool change, etc., and the frequency at which each happens. These are addressed under the column labeled, "Noncyclic Tasks." Capture the specific needs of the operation. The total time should reflect periodic time allocation for these activities.

3. Machine no.: Fill in the appropriate machine numbers

Process Design Analysis Sheet

Measure	Current	Proposed
Floor space (square ft)		
Total part travel (linear ft)		
Number of operators		
Number of support personnel		
Standard work in process		
Units/labor hour		
Cost/piece		
Manufacturing lead time		
5S rating		
Value-added ratio		
Scrap rate (parts per million)		

Figure 7-11.

Value-adding Determination

Product/component:

Quoted lead time (days):

Batch size:

Manufacturing lead time (days):

Value-adding operations	Time/piece
1	
2	
3	
4	
5	
6	
7	
8	
9	
10	
11	
12	
Total value-added time	

$$\text{Value-added \%} = \frac{\text{Value-added time}}{\text{Manufacturing lead time}} \times 100\% = \boxed{}$$

Figure 7-12.

Process Capacity Table

Net operating time (T_o) =

Daily quantity required (T_q) =

Date:

Line:

Part #:

Part name:

Page _____ of _____

Maximum output per day:

Step No.	Process Description	Machine No.	Walk Time	Base Time			Non-cyclic Tasks			Total Time (G = C + F)	Total Capacity (H = T_o/G)	Comments
				Manual Time (A)	Automatic Time (B)	Machine Cycle Time (C = A + B)	No. of Pieces per Change (D)	Time to Change (E)	Time per Piece (F = E/D)			

Figure 7-13.

as assigned on the Standard Work Sheet.

4. Calculate base time.

    a. Manual time (*A*): measure and then enter the hands-on time it takes for the operator to perform the operation on the machine.

    b. Automatic time (*B*): measure and then enter the time needed for the machine to process the work. Note: the operator's wait time may be shown if his or her work is performed internal to the machine's cycle time.

    c. Machine cycle time (*C*): this is the time it takes to complete one part (or two if processed two at a time) on the process. Usually,

    $$C = A + B \qquad \text{(Eq. 7-3)}$$

    For operations occurring with a specific frequency, enter the manual work time for one workpiece.

5. List non-cyclic tasks. These are tasks that were noted in step 2c. They are done at a given frequency. This frequency can be based on the number of pieces, operating hours, or it can be once a day or per shift.

    a. Number of pieces per change (*D*): this is the number of pieces that can be made in between the occurrences of this activity.

    b. Time to change (*E*): this is the amount of time consumed in performing the task.

    c. Time per piece (*F*): this is the amount of time to change allocated to each individual piece processed after the activity.

    $$F = E/D \qquad \text{(Eq. 7-4)}$$

6. Calculate the total time (*G*).

    $$G = C + F \qquad \text{(Eq. 7-5)}$$

7. Total capacity (*H*): this is the quantity of parts that can be produced within the limit of the production hours (T_o) allocated to this part's production.

    $$H = T_o/G \qquad \text{(Eq. 7-6)}$$

A Flow Layout Sheet or spaghetti diagram, such as the one shown in Figure 7-14, is also required to document the current state. Completing

Flow Layout Sheet
Production in Specialized Departments
Level One

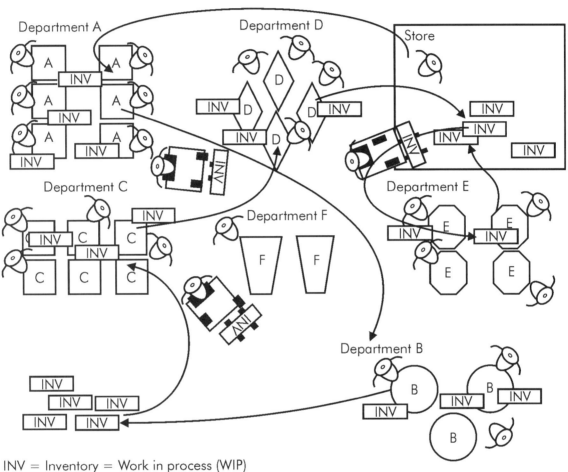

INV = Inventory = Work in process (WIP)

Figure 7-14.

this, in addition to the Process Design Analysis Sheet, Value-adding Determination, and Process Design Analysis Sheet documents the base data. This will help the team clearly see the condition of the production line and consider the possibilities. An understanding of the activities involved, in addition to the documented details of the current state, is absolutely necessary if improvements are to be made. A plan for tomorrow can not be made until the team knows exactly where the process is today.

STEP 2: FUTURE STATE MAPPING

Once the data is collected and documented for the current state, then it is time for the team to dig in and brainstorm on improvements. The team leader uses the checklist in Figure 7-15 to guide the process of creating a future state map.

The Target: Waste (Muda)

In creating the future state map, the current map is reviewed with an eye toward waste elimination. Anything that adds cost without adding value is considered waste. Here are the 10 forms of muda the team needs to keep a watchful eye for:

1. Waste from overproducing

2. Waste of time (waiting)

3. Waste from transporting

4. Waste from over-processing (complicated/complex process)

5. Waste of inventory

6. Waste of motion (worker movements at workstation)

7. Waste caused by defects and rework

8. Human underutilization

9. Improper use of computers

10. Working to the wrong metrics

Brainstorming

With the hands-on knowledge gained from the current state

Future State Mapping Checklist (to be completed by team leader)

❑ Ask, "What would this process be if it were waste-free?"

❑ Review the 10 forms of muda (waste). Is there any here?

❑ Brainstorm—use a board to write down all ideas and then categorize them.

❑ Using the Flow Layout Sheet (see Figure 7-14) from the current state mapping, cut and paste a new proposed layout.

❑ Look at the details of the rearrangement, what obstacles are there?

❑ Select the best-choice alternative and develop a new layout.

❑ Complete the Process Design Analysis Sheet for the new process (see Figure 7-11).

❑ Meet with the operators to collaborate on new ideas.

Figure 7-15.

mapping, the team will have many improvement ideas to bring forward. All ideas and alternatives should be documented. Similar ideas are grouped, along with the pros and cons of each. At this point, the team should be careful not to get bogged down in details—in other words, they should view improvements at the 10,000-ft level first.

The team continues brainstorming until all alternatives are exhausted. Each time there are new suggestions, the team proceeds out to the shop floor to lay out the design on the floor, full scale. Using the current state layout, team members cut and paste the machines into the new configuration, trying different iterations of each theme. Cardboard is used to represent actual machines if necessary.

During the brainstorming process there is constant evaluation of the new process versus the old. The data from the current state Process Design Analysis Sheet is indispensable to determine the best new process. Simply stated, the best new process will have the best new numbers in comparison to the current process.

Once the team agrees on the best flow and overall layout, the details of how to make it happen are documented. This includes instructions detailing the machines to be moved, the utilities required to be disconnected and reconnected, etc. The maintenance person on each team reviews the plan so that if there are problems in the new design, they can be addressed immediately. If there is not a maintenance person on the team, it is advisable that he or she be consulted before implementing the new layout. To help determine all the requirements of the new process, the team leader uses the checklist in Figure 7-16 to guide the team.

Standard Work Instructions

Standard work instructions are developed during the brainstorming sessions that arrive at the final rendition of the newly designed cell. They must comply with all International Organization for Standardization (ISO) standards, Quality Standards (QS), Military (MIL) specifications, or other regulating agencies or standards bodies, as determined by the customers' policies and requirements. In addition, they must comply with Occupational Safety and Health Administration

**New Process Requirements
Checklist
(to be completed by team leader)**

❑ Clean the area of focus, leaving only the essentials needed to perform the "new" tasks. Mark the floor.

❑ Make a detailed layout with instructions for maintenance personnel so they can make the moves during the night.

❑ Rearrange the process to include the work in process (WIP) needed, as well as support functions required for changeovers and tools.

❑ Continue to brainstorm with the team. Ask the operators for their input and critique of the new process.

❑ Think outside of the box—be daring!

Figure 7-16.

(OSHA) rules and guidelines. The details of the work instructions are transferred to a Standard Work Combination Sheet, such as the one shown in Figure 7-17. Instructions for its completion are as follows.

1. Heading information: fill in from left to right.

   a. Part no.: fill in the part number for the process being documented. Each Standard Work Combination Sheet represents a separate part number's process. One must be done for each operator.

   b. Process name: fill in the description of the operation being performed.

   c. Effective date: enter the date when this Standard Work Combination is to be put into effect.

   d. Cell: enter the name of the cell in which this operation takes place.

   e. Quantity per shift: this is the amount of the part number listed in "1a" that will be made in a shift. This number was needed to calculate the takt time for the Standard Work Sheet and can be found there.

   f. Takt time: this is the rate at which this part/assembly must be performed to meet daily customer demand. This number was also needed for the Standard Work Sheet and can be found there.

   g. Gap: this is the difference between the operator's

Standard Work Combination Sheet

Page	of		Operator:
Part no.:		Quantity per shift:	
Process name:		Takt time:	
		Gap:	

Cell:

Effective date:

Manual ———
Auto. ·······
Walking 〜
Waiting ↕

Seq. No.	Description of Operation	Time Elements			Cumulative Operating Time (seconds)
		Manual	Auto.	Walk	5" 10" 15" 20" 25" 30" 35" 40" 45" 50" 55" 60" 65" 70" 75" 80" 85" 90" 95"
Totals					

Figure 7-17.

cycle time and the takt time for the part/assembly. The number must be positive if the sequence is to supply the quantity required per day/shift.

h. Operator: just as each machine is to be numbered, so are the operators. Enter the number of the operator.

2. Sequence no.: fill in the sequence number of each component task assigned to this operator. These numbers should match those used on the Time Observation Sheet for the same operation.

3. Description of operation: in as much detail as possible, enter a description of the sequenced activity. Use expressions made up of a present-tense verb and its direct object, for example, "press button." Add in the machine number if it is available.

4. Record the time elements.

    a. Manual: manual work time is the amount of operator activity time for this sequence step as shown on

the Time Observation Sheet.

    b. Auto.: automatic machine cycle time is the amount of unassisted machine cycle time. If the operator must attend the machine, this should be considered manual time.

    c. Walk: walking time is the time it takes for the operator to move from one station to the next. Do not distinguish between whether or not the operator is carrying something. Round the time off to the nearest second. Leave this space blank if there is no walking time assignable to this step.

    d. Totals: enter the total times at the bottom of each column.

5. Chart the cumulative operating time (in seconds).

    a. Indicate manual work time by a solid line.

    b. Indicate automatic machine time by a dotted line.

    c. Indicate walking time by a wavy line.

d. Indicate waiting time by a line with arrows on each end.

6. Draw the takt time line. A red line is drawn vertically on the chart indicating the takt time value. This should be the same as the takt time value indicated at the top of the sheet.

An example of a completed Standard Work Combination Sheet is shown in Figure 7-18.

Manual on Work Direction

A *Manual on Work Direction* must be created, comprising all of the standard work instructions for a given process. Documenting work instructions ensures there is no question as to how tasks should be performed. Deviations from work instructions are *never* allowed. Work instructions are updated according to the policies of each company, in compliance with the provisions set forth by regulating and standards bodies. Figure 7-19 is a form blank from a *Manual on Work Direction*. Instructions for its completion are as follows.

1. Heading information: fill it in from left to right.

a. Fill in the name of the area manager or the area's manufacturing engineer.

b. Floor foreman: this would normally be the department foreman.

c. Group leader: this is normally the leader of the group to which these instructions pertain.

d. Part number: this is the same as the part number from the Standard Work Combination Sheet.

e. Part name: this is the same as the part name on the Standard Work Combination Sheet.

f. Quantity: this is the daily/shift total of the part needed per day. This number was recorded on the Standard Work Combination Sheet and can be found there.

g. Customers: record the customers for this part, and what the ratios are for each out of 100 pieces. For example, if the output is split between two

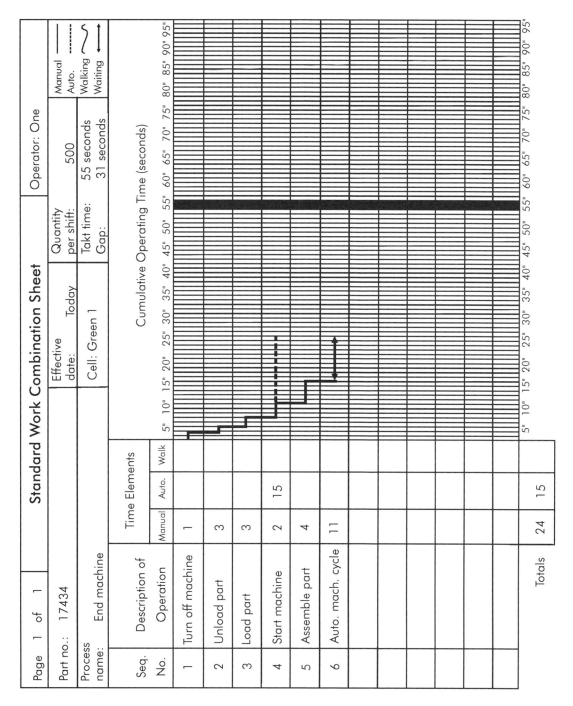

Standard Work Combination Sheet

Page 1 of 1		Operator: One

Part no.: 17434	Effective date: Today	Quantity per shift: 500	
Process name: End machine	Cell: Green 1	Takt time: 55 seconds	Gap: 31 seconds

Time Elements

Seq. No.	Description of Operation	Manual	Auto.	Walk
1	Turn off machine	1		
2	Unload part	3		
3	Load part	3		
4	Start machine	2	15	
5	Assemble part	4		
6	Auto. mach. cycle	11		
	Totals	24	15	

Cumulative Operating Time (seconds)

Manual ———
Auto. --------
Walking ⌒
Waiting ↕

Figure 7-18.

Manual on Work Direction

Page ____ of ____

Area manager:	Floor foreman:	Group leader:	Part number:	Quantity:	Team:	Operator:
			Part name:	Customers:		

Flow Diagram

Takt Time
Standard WIP
Net Operating Time

Step No.	Work Content	Quality Check	Type	Critical Concerns	Operating Time Min. Sec.															

Total

Figure 7-19.

customers, the breakdown number would be 50/50.

h. Team: record the name of the team doing the production work described by this instruction sheet.

i. Operator: insert the name/number of the operator performing the task list described on this sheet.

2. Step no.: fill in the sequence number of each component task assigned to this operator. The sequence numbers should match the step numbers recorded on the Time Observation Sheet for the same operation.

3. Task: provide a description of activities to be performed at each workstation of the cell, allocating one station per line.

4. Quality check: record the frequency at which quality checks must be performed during production of this part at this process step. Frequency is expressed as a ratio, for example, 100% is shown as 1/1; one in ten is shown as 1/10.

5. Quality type: describe the type of inspection along with

identifying the gage number/designator used to perform the task.

6. Critical concerns: information placed here applies to special or critical conditions to be noted before, during, and/or after running the process. Notes can apply to cyclic as well as non-cyclic tasks.

7. Operating time: this is the total amount of elapsed time allotted to perform this sequence step. It is totaled at the bottom of the sheet to see if it exceeds the takt time allowed for this particular product.

8. Flow diagram: in the open rectangular space running along the right side of this form, enter the layout from the Standard Work Sheet along with the other information asked for, which can be transcribed from that source.

Operator's Detailed Instruction Sheet

Figure 7-20 is a form blank designed to provide detailed work

Operator's Detailed Instruction Sheet			
Machine number:	Part number:	Part name:	ODIS number:
Machine name:	ODIS rev.	Approval:	Page ____ of ____
Prepared by:	Part rev.	Date revised:	Operation no. ____ of ____

Quality

Standardized Work Description

Activity No.

Figure 7-20.

Kaizen Event Implementation Manual

instructions for the operator. It is completed as follows.

1. Heading information: fill in from left to right.

    a. Machine number: the machine's serial number or process sheet designation is recorded here.

    b. Machine name: enter the machine's description.

    c. Prepared by: this is normally the leader of the group to which these instructions pertain.

    d. Part number: this is the same as the part number from the Standard Work Combination Sheet.

    e. ODIS rev.: this is the Operator's Detailed Instruction Sheet revision number used in the event this document requires revision control tracking. The revision letter designation for the form is placed here.

    f. Part rev.: this letter designation comes from the latest part blueprint. The revision date of the part letter being processed per

this set of instructions is also entered here. If the ODIS is not a controlled document, fields "e" and "f" are not required.

    g. Part number: fill in the part number for the process being documented.

    h. Approval: if required, a sign-off signature can be entered here.

    i. Date revised: enter the implementation date of the last revision.

    j. ODIS number: the revision number of the form goes here. Again, if the ODIS is not a controlled document, this field is not required.

    k. Page: this field is applicable if there are multiple pages of instructions for this activity/operation.

    l. Operation no.: the operation number for this activity in the process flow is listed here.

2. Activity no.: this is the sequence number assigned to each component task for this operator. The sequence

numbers should match those used on the Time Observation Sheet for the same operation.

3. Standardized work description: a full description of the operator's steps is recorded here. These are the steps the operator will follow exactly when processing the listed part at the operation indicated in the heading.

4. Quality: this space is used for sketches, drawings, or photos of the quality measurement of this particular part on this operation. It is also an area for visual control, showing exactly what is done at each step via visual representation.

STEP 3: NEW PROCESS IMPLEMENTATION

By Wednesday night, the new layout should be drawn up and ready for the maintenance people so they can move the machines and equipment overnight. In setting up the new process, as many of the ideas as possible are implemented. Those items that can not be addressed at this time go on the follow-up sheet for the event coordinator's attention. On Thursday morning there is an evaluation of the changes made overnight and a plan is made for completing the tasks left undone.

Before the team can adjourn Thursday night, the following assignments need to be completed:

• All operators must be trained in the new methods and the cell must be running good product at the improved efficiency.

• All safety issues must be resolved.

• The follow-up (30-day) list must be compiled.

• All documentation must be completed (ISO 9000).

Once the operators are able to reasonably operate the cell, each station/operator is retimed. The team continues to refine the cell and gather the new data for the Process Design Analysis Sheet (see Figure 7-11) until optimal results are achieved. The Value-adding Determination (see Figure 7-12) will be needed to complete the new Process Design Analysis Sheet. Next, a Standard Work Combination Sheet (see Figure 7-17) is completed.

The team leader uses the checklist in Figure 7-21 to guide the team as it verifies and documents the re-

---

**New Process
Verification Checklist
(to be completed by team leader)**

☐ Talk to the operators. Test out the new process.

☐ Observe new cycle times and note any problems.

☐ Check for any possible safety issues.

☐ Is there enough work in process (WIP) at the proper locations?

☐ Complete the Standard Work Combination Sheet (see Figure 7-17).

☐ Redo the Time Observation Sheet (see Figure 7-9).

☐ Itemize all implemented improvements. Determine the costs of implementation.

☐ Calculate all savings—including part travel, operator travel, throughput time, operator savings, square footage, etc.

Figure 7-21.

sentation by using the checklist in Figure 7-22. By late on Thursday afternoon the team should be ready to work on the presentation. Not everyone will be able to participate at this time, but it is a good idea to get the presentation started as soon as possible.

A new 5S survey (see Figure 7-7) may be conducted so a comparison can be made to the beginning 5S condition.

Before adjourning on Thursday, the final presentation should be complete and include the following for both the old and new process:

We're out of sight!

sults of the improvements. This information will be needed to prepare the report-out presentation and finalize standard work instructions.

STEP 4: REPORT-OUT PRESENTATION

The team leader can assess the team's readiness to begin the pre-

---

Report-out Preparation Checklist (to be completed by team leader)

❏ All operators are trained on the new process.

❏ The process is actually running and producing good parts at the cycle times established.

❏ Hard copies of the presentation are complete with overheads.

❏ Review Process Design Analysis Sheet (see Figure 7-11).

❏ All Standard Work Sheets (see Figure 7-3) are complete with takt times.

❏ Safety improvements are made (three per day or one per team member).

❏ List possible future improvements.

❏ All analysis work is complete with comparisons of old and new process plotted on charts.

❏ New layout is complete.

❏ Costs/benefits calculations are figured and documented.

❏ Follow-up ("30-day") list is compiled.

❏ All necessary documentation (ISO 9000) is complete.

Figure 7-22.

- Process Design Analysis Sheet,
- Standard Work Sheets,
- Process Capacity Table,
- takt time calculation,

- floor layout,
- Flow Layout Sheet (spaghetti diagram),
- Standard Work Combination Sheets for each operator/station,
- illustrations to explain the improvements,
- before and after videos or digital photos, and
- additional observations.

Early on Friday morning, the team should gather to rehearse the presentation. Team presentations should be no longer than 20 minutes each, exclusive of questions. Each team member participates, even if only in a small way. The presentations represent a true team effort.

It is recommended for the team leader to flip the overheads or index the monitor so that each person does not need to do so.

At 9:00 a.m., the event coordinator begins by introducing the visitors and speakers. After the quick introductory speeches, the presentations begin. Then the event coordinator asks each team member to tell what they learned or got out of the event. Comments by each person should be limited to less than a minute so the session can wrap up by 11:00 a.m. and celebration can begin.

An Event Evaluation Form, such as the one shown in Figure 7-23, should be passed out for all the participants to complete. Some companies like the audience to fill one out too.

Event Evaluation Form

Date:	Company:	Coordinator:
Name:	Event location:	Team leader:
Phone:	Product line:	Consultant:
E-mail:	Team name:	Plant manager:

1. What was your overall impression of the event?

_____
_____
_____

2. Describe the best or most useful part of the event:

_____
_____
_____

3. What would you change about the event to make it more useful?

_____
_____
_____

4. Would you like to participate in another event? If not, please explain why.

_____
_____
_____

5. Did the event accomplish all that was intended? Could more have been done?
   If so, please explain.

_____
_____
_____

6. How were you treated? Could you give your opinions freely?

_____
_____
_____

	Poor									Excellent
7. Please rate the instructor:	1	2	3	4	5	6	7	8	9	10
8. Please rate the team leader:	1	2	3	4	5	6	7	8	9	10
9. Quality of training material:	1	2	3	4	5	6	7	8	9	10
10. Usefulness to the company:	1	2	3	4	5	6	7	8	9	10

Additional comments:

_____
_____

Figure 7-23.

Eight

After the Event

CELEBRATION

With the hard work done, the time for recognition and celebration has arrived. For the event, the team may have been given distinguishing hats or shirts, but were afraid to wear them. Now that all is done and a success, the teams should wear them with pride!

It is customary to award certificates with photos to each team member, as well as take photographs at the celebration party. Some events give special recognition awards to the participant who traveled the farthest, or the team member who got the dirtiest, or something similar. Such awards allow everyone to share in the lighthearted aspects of the event.

FOLLOW-UP (30-DAY) LIST

The kaizen team should implement as many of the improvements as possible during the event. However, it is common for there to be unfinished business that must be completed afterward. These items are put on the follow-up list to be completed within 30 days. The real success of the event will be measured later, after all the recommendations have been implemented.

As part of the follow-up, the event coordinator must check on any regulatory issues (Food and Drug Administration [FDA], Occupational Safety and Health Administration [OSHA], etc.) that must be resolved, ensuring all forms are filled out and that the company is compliant with the rules.

The event coordinator prioritizes the follow-up list and assigns specific tasks to individuals. A Gantt chart, such as the one shown in Figure 8-1, is useful for organizing what needs to be done. It is the event coordinator's responsibility to see that tasks are completed in a timely manner. A review meeting should be scheduled for one week later to monitor the results. Any issues that require outside assistance should be assigned to the appropriate staff member to follow-up on and report back the following week.

Completing the "to do" list shows everyone that the company is serious about implementing suggestions

for improvement. It also demonstrates the company's dedication to achieving favorable results and management's faith in the people on the teams. The first task of a new event will be to revisit the last event's 30-day list to see if all the pending tasks were completed. A new event should not begin until all items from the previous event are finished.

MEET WITH THE EXECUTIVE TEAM

Immediately after the celebration, the executive team is drawn together by the event coordinator to thoroughly review the event and see first-hand, the improvements. A union executive is usually in attendance. The team is asked if there were any surprises or failures and if the goals and objectives of the event were met. Everyone discusses ideas for improvement and the action items are noted for implementation.

FOLLOW-UP WITH OPERATORS

The operators on the affected lines should be contacted as soon as possible after the event by the event coordinator. Within the following week, they should be asked for their

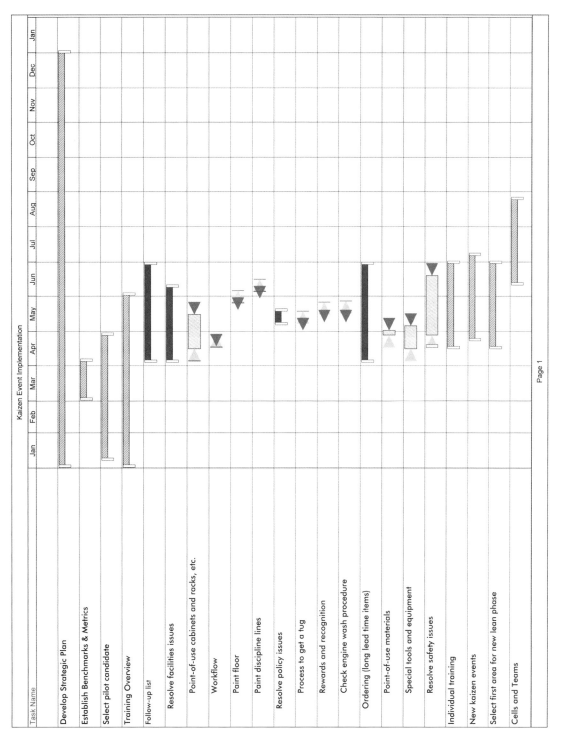

Figure 8-1.

evaluation of the changes and their thoughts about the event. Suggestions or complaints should be documented and given as feedback to the team leaders. This information will be invaluable for the improvement of future events. As a result, subsequent events will become progressively better and easier to run.

In addition, the operators should be part of a weekly meeting facilitated by the event coordinator to measure the amount of acceptance to the new system. They may have ideas and suggestions that can correct flaws in the original cell design. Operators will try harder than anyone to make their ideas work. They should be given the chance to be part of the change.

REVIEW THE EVALUATION FORMS

Kaizen events are dynamic; no two are alike. Similarly, the solicited comments and evaluations given by participants on Event Evaluation Forms (see Figure 7-23), differ from person to person and event to event. To measure the event's success and spawn ideas for improvement, the executive team should thoroughly review the evaluation forms and

noted comments. A comparison should be made to other events (unless this is the first one) to see the progress and common threads. Improvement ideas should be documented so they can be revisited for the next event.

In addition, the information on the evaluation forms is invaluable to those responsible for the success of kaizen events as a means to measure the performance of individuals and teams. Likewise, consultants and event coordinators can use the feedback to measure their personal success. Team leaders can also learn a lot from reviewing the information.

ONGOING COMMUNICATION

Thirty days after the event, the event coordinator formally pub-

lishes the results of the kaizen event for all to see. In the results, a comparison is made to the old standards, showing the accumulated savings to date. A 12-month projection of the expected savings is documented and tracked weekly. (Things that are tracked usually improve.)

In the affected area, updates should be posted on a regular basis so the improvements can be seen as permanent and not just temporary.

The reassignment of the displaced operators should be made known to all the plant personnel. (None should have been released or laid-off). All displaced workers are performing new functions, which allow the use of their newly acquired skills, thanks to the kaizen training.

Hereafter, everyone must be constantly reminded that kaizen goes on forever!

Nine

Kaizen in a One-piece Flow, Cellular Operation

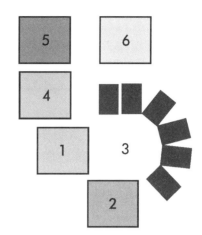

LEAN CELL POLICIES

The following policies are applicable to a molding cell specifically. However, they may be adapted to any cellular operation. It is a good idea to keep cell policies posted in sight for all workers to see.

1. There must be ongoing one-piece flow at all times in the cell, between all workstations, depending on the cable characteristics:

   • One piece will be considered as the mold with its number of cavities.

   • One piece also will be considered a sub-multiple of the number of cavities.

   • One-piece flow is defined as "one piece at a time."

   • Certain activities requiring the accumulation of parts, such as to allow drying time for glue or curing time for adhesives, will be designed with a "curtain effect." This allows for the accumulation of part batches to and from the secondary process, which is usually performed off-line.

2. The cell must be run with the correct amount of operators, per its design. You may NOT use more or fewer operators than the number required by the cell's design. A change to the staffing requires that the cell be rebalanced and a new "standard" established for efficiency and costing reasons.

3. All operators in a cell will perform their work activities standing. Chairs will be used only by those workers with medical problems. All workbenches will be at an ergonomically correct height. All physical activities will be ergonomically evaluated to ensure the correct movements of workers.

4. Nowhere in the cell, at any time, is material permitted to be reworked later. All unacceptable material will have to be reworked at the moment the failure occurs and registered as such. Material that does not meet the tolerances of acceptable rework must be discarded immediately.

5. Whenever there is a change of order to a part number with different characteristics, the cell must be completely emptied. The packed materials as well as scrap and all information regarding the previous part number will be completely removed from the cell before the next part number starts running.

6. Never accept a deviate part from a previous workstation; never make a deviate part; and never pass on a deviate part. If you notice a deviation occurring, you are to stop production immediately and call attention to the deviate part. Make a note of where the deviate part came from and why it deviates from the standard. Then decide whether or not the part can be immediately reworked. If not, remove it at once to a designated scrap receptacle.

7. The correct Process Sheet, Standard Work Combination Sheet and quality alerts must be posted within the cell. These should be color-coded for each workstation to prevent the use of incorrect instructions.

8. Respect at all times the feelings and thoughts of others.

9. Keep an open mind to change.

10. Keep a positive attitude.

11. Never look to blame someone; look for solutions instead.

12. There are no ranks or positions in this system. Everyone has the same voice and vote.

13. Never have doubts. There are no such things as stupid questions.

14. Instead of trying to plan for perfection, learn by doing and making errors, and then correct those errors.

15. All cells operate with work teams and decisions are made democratically.

16. A team leader must be named for the cell. This person is usually nominated by the cell's quality champion.

17. The cell must have a 5S champion.

18. A cell with equipment that must be changed when switching from one part number to another must have a single-minute exchange of die (SMED) champion. This person will facilitate quick changeovers and track and post progress in the cell.

19. The cell must have a total productive maintenance (TPM) champion.

20. The role of Water Spider (someone to perform material handling and stocking) must be assigned. This position may rotate among the team members.

21. The cell team must have designated people responsible for gathering, posting, and reporting the six key measurement metrics: productivity, functional planned preventive maintenance (PPM), electrical PPM, downtime, starts, and SMED results.

22. Operators must rotate their workstations at least once per shift, for an equal amount of time.

23. Kanbans can be used to facilitate process flow.

   • A kanban is a physical device and its capacity is defined physically and visually.

   • Kanban must be included in the process flow to balance part production.

   • Kanban must be documented in the process flow for the part number produced.

• Kanban will not exceed more than four times the number of mold cavities.

24. All information regarding the cell, developed in it, or coming from external sources and needed for production, will be concentrated in the information system of the corresponding cell. This includes 5S reports, and tracking and results of the six basic metrics.

25. The team must start performing a flex test on all cables that will be electrically tested. After a period of one month, and registering zero failures of the electric test on the corresponding cell indicator, the team can stop performing the flex test. However, if there is a failure of an electric test of any kind, the flex test operation must be reinstated until another month passes by without any failure.

26. There will be no variations or deviations from any established process by anyone for any reason, unless approved and documented by management.

ROLES IN THE LEAN CELL ENVIRONMENT

Lean Champion

The lean champion is responsible for promoting the integration of the new lean cell and reporting the details to the plant manager and the director of continuous improvement. He or she is responsible for managing and acquiring the physical resources within the budget for the lean system's development or conversion. This includes the acquisition of software used in different lean applications in the plant.

Along with the plant manager, the lean champion plays the role of psychologist and leader of the work force, enforcing lean policies in all areas. In this role, he or she is responsible for detecting behaviors or activities of regression in the plant and seeing to their elimination. The lean champion is also an active participant in the rewards system for zero defects in all lean cells of the plant.

In collaboration with HR staff, the lean champion interviews and recruits members for new teams as required. He or she verifies the employee involvement program, managing the requests and suggestions boxes of all the teams/lean cells in the plant. All personnel are expected to exhibit lean thinking and strive to continuously improve work processes.

Development and Training

The lean champion collaborates with HR and plant management to develop a lean training program and roll-out schedule for the plant. He or she maintains the lean training material and standardizes what is taught for all levels of workers.

In a daily hands-on role, the lean champion acts as a driver, providing assistance in the development and transformation of a new lean cell. He or she trains the teams as required, assuring the use of lean policies across the plant.

The lean champion works with cells that have not accomplished lean objectives. Kaizen events are scheduled therein and the lean champion follows up on the improvements to make sure there is no lapse in implementation.

Information and Verification

The lean champion is responsible for gathering and integrating information on the status of lean imple-

mentation throughout the plant, including the verification of output from software that tracks performance to metrics. Each week a report is presented to the plant manager and director of continuous improvement. In ongoing communications with the lean cells and in collaboration with HR, the lean champion also provides teams with the results of evaluations and schedules appointments with managers for the rejected team members. Team members are also kept advised about technical problems found in the work area, as well as the status of lean implementation plant-wide.

In charge of updating system policies once they are proven to work correctly, the lean champion controls the forms and documentation related to system implementation and development. He or she is also responsible for verification that the cells are established under the lean standards and using the appropriate metrics. This includes verification of the parts-quantity analysis for conversion to the lean system.

Managers/Supervisors

To facilitate lean cell roll-out on the plant floor, a schedule of meetings with specific objectives is set for the cell teams. Attendance at the meetings is not optional and exemption will only be allowed in exceptional cases.

A supervisor is usually assigned to a cell, but he or she is considered to have the same rank and voice as any other team member in the cell. This person is *not* the boss. Although the supervisory role carries with it the authority to validate the behavior code of the team and to validate internal work guidelines, in the lean environment it is recommended for this person to take on a conciliatory position rather than an authoritarian one.

The first and most important function of the supervisor is to monitor and create cohesion within the team. Acting as an educator and mentor, the supervisor provides leadership and guidance, and is the "conscience" of the team.

Specific supervisory responsibilities include:

- Keep the flow exactly as designed and analyze the information provided to the cell by the process engineer. Sign the corresponding form(s) along with the rest of the team.

- Coordinate between the first and second shifts.

- Reassign "floating" operators from the team to other cells when there is a part number that does not require the total number of operators available.

- Implement new physical or organizational systems.

- Detect and resolve conflicts in the most fluid way possible.

- Participate in the daily activity and operation of the lean cell as a dynamic force and example.

- Advise and console workers who are rejected by their team.

When a lean cell begins production, the team is required to give daily updates to the responsible supervisor for a period no fewer than two weeks. This facilitates the discussion of problems and suggestions for improving the performance of the cell. Even after the two-week initial period it is a good idea for the supervisor to set weekly team meetings. At these meetings the six measurement indicators are exposed for discussion so that actions can be taken to improve the team's performance in problem areas. In the case of an internal or external rejection, the supervisor must schedule a meeting with the team on the same day the rejection takes place or the day after, and the manager must be present.

A team member may require reassignment or removal from a specific team for justified reasons. However, one month prior to the startup of the cell, teams have already been formed and once an operator has decided to be on a team, he or she cannot ask to be removed so close to startup. This one-month period of time gives team members the chance to work with one another, comprehend the cell's functioning, and overcome the initial chaos that normally occurs. Thus, it is unlikely that reassignment or removal from a team will happen in this period. But an operator who does not follow the behavior code after several warnings and who has been evaluated by the management as a negative profile will be replaced by another operator.

After the one-month initial period after the cell is started, team member removal or replacement may occur if:

- The team member requests to be removed, as long as he or she has justified reasons evaluated by the production unit.

- The request for removal/replacement of a specific team member comes from the team facilitator or the leader acting as a spokesperson for the team.

- The behavior code has been breached by a specific team member. The recommendation for removal from the team should be made democratically within the team and should not be the exclusive decision of the leader.

- The supervisor has performed a formal evaluation of the team and determined that a certain team member should be removed because he or she is a burden to the work team instead of a support. If the evaluation score is 50% or less, that member may be removed to another team.

When a team member is removed from a cell after an evaluation, he or she will be required by the production manager to attend a meeting the next day. The purpose of this meeting will be to encourage improvement and discuss assignment to a new team.

When a new team member is enrolled on a team after the initial two-week startup period, he or she cannot be removed from the team for a minimum period of one week. After that period, the team members will decide democratically, in a meeting, if the new member is an appropriate addition to the team. Once the new member is accepted, he or she will be entitled to the same privileges as other team members.

Process Engineer

The process engineer is responsible for evaluating the results of the 5S audits of all cells. He or she coordinates a one-hour meeting once a week with all the 5S champions whose cells obtained a score lower than 80 points so that proper corrective action can be taken. The supervisors of the affected cells determine the time for the meeting. To raise the 5S score in the next audit, the process engineer helps to carry out the necessary actions along with the audited team.

Responsible for auditing one or several teams in each cell once a week, the process engineer must observe that each 5S champion has divulged the 5S information correctly.

He or she is also responsible for analyzing and evaluating the process flows, time taking, balancing, and completing the Standard Work Combination Sheets, which must be provided to the cells. This information will be standardized throughout the plant. Thus it must be written on the forms established specifically for capturing the information.

After a kaizen event, during new "lean" cell implementation, the supervisor will coordinate with the process engineer to intensely observe the cell for a period of no fewer than two weeks. The cell must not be out of observation for more than one hour during this period. As a result of observations, the process engineer may make adjustments to the workload at each workstation or modify all or portions of the operation.

Quality Engineer

The quality engineer is responsible for gathering information regarding internal and/or external rejects that occur within the period of one week throughout the plant.

It is a requirement that the quality champions from each section attend a one-hour meeting once a week, which is coordinated by the quality engineer. At the meeting, each attendee is provided with information regarding a problem and its solution. The supervisor of the section determines the time for the meeting. The quality engineer is responsible for coordinating the necessary efforts to resolve the quality problem and responds to all requests of the teams in this regard. In addition, he or she is responsible for auditing one or several teams once a week to observe if the quality champions have divulged the quality information correctly.

The quality engineer also audits the processes in each cell to determine if they are operating as designed. He or she recommends areas where poka-yokes should be installed or where a poka-yoke kaizen event should take place. Subsequently, the quality engineer may conduct poka-yoke events with the cooperation and consent of the lean champion.

Production Scheduler

To begin, the production schedule must be available for updating in the information system of the cell. The production scheduler coordinates efforts with the cell's SMED champion, sharing the production priorities and status, the part sequence required by customers, and performance on delivery information. To this end, the production scheduler coordinates a meeting once a week in the cells where delivery performance is less than 90%. The supervisor of the cell determines the meeting time. The SMED champion works to reduce changeover times, so more production can be run; either by running smaller kanban or just being able to run more of the right parts because of added capacity.

Teams

In addition to complying with the lean cell policies, team members are expected to:

- Exchange positions on a daily basis, excluding the position of Water Spider, which takes place on a weekly basis.

- Keep record of the metric indicators of the cell on a daily basis.

- Give a weekly update of the trend of the indicators to appropriate managers/supervisors.

- Frequently submit ideas/requests to the suggestions box.

• Democratically elect the champions of the cell.

Once it is demonstrated that the cell is able to meet its objectives for productivity, quality, and delivery, all the team members must switch positions in the new cell at least once during a shift and for equivalent periods of time. This will ensure everyone becomes cross-trained on all the tasks performed within the cell.

When team members do not have enough skill in the new operation assigned, the switch can be done the first week for a period of one hour to allow them to get acclimated to the new tasks. Team members are moved to an operation where they feel slower or more insecure in their ability to perform it. When the hour expires, they return to their original assigned operation.

Every succeeding week the team members change operations for one additional hour until they get to work in two positions for equivalent periods of time during the shift without adversely affecting the indicators of the cell.

Team Leader

The team leader is responsible for motivating the lean cell team to reach its goals. This person must possess natural leadership characteristics. He or she acts as team spokesperson when participating in meetings with quality champions of other lean cells to eliminate potential or existing problems or when reporting to management or supervision.

Within the team, the team leader is the first to address general doubts, provide explanation, or resolve conflicts among team members. He or she takes immediate action when a quality problem exists. Another key responsibility is the evaluation of team member performance to the lean metrics.

5S Champion

It is the responsibility of the 5S champion to coordinate and audit the cleaning activities of the lean cell to maintain a score higher than 80 points. He or she is expected to collaborate with the 5S champions of other cells to develop improvement plans when audit scores are less than 80 points.

The 5S champion maintains the cleaning equipment and supplies provided to the cell and makes sure that daily cleaning tasks are performed as scheduled. Ideas for improvement are entered into a log for later implementation.

SMED Champion

The single-minute exchange of dies (SMED) champion coordinates changeover activities in the cell. The goal is to perform changeover in less than six minutes. He or she maintains control of the production schedule for the cell and joins efforts with the Water Spider on a daily basis. A record is kept of the production orders completed and of changeover results. The SMED champion collaborates with other SMED champions to make improvements when delivery performance is less than 90%.

It is the responsibility of the SMED champion to review the equipment, tooling, and people required in the cell to produce customer orders. The operation is balanced daily by adjusting the number of operators and sequence of part numbers produced.

TPM Champion

The total productive maintenance (TPM) champion is responsible for the tools and spare parts provided to the cell, and for maintaining their orderly presence. He or she evaluates the condition of the machines working in the cell and assigns an overall equipment effectiveness (OEE) ratio to each one. The main functions of the TPM champion are to perform basic preventive maintenance on the equipment as scheduled and track OEE on a weekly report.

Human Resources

It is the job of human resources (HR) to continually manage the human and physical resources needed to develop the lean cell system. In this endeavor, the roles of human resources staff include that of psychologists, mentors, and policy enforcers for all persons working under the new lean system. HR staff work as advisors to the cells and have the authority to resolve conflicts within the system.

Development and Training

The human resources department approves and performs training on new physical or organizational systems designed to develop the new lean system. It is responsible for driving and promoting the intellectual development of workers.

HR staff members participate in the daily activities of the cells and are seen as a dynamic force, exemplifying and promoting lean and the concept of participative management.

HR also participates in selecting the appropriate candidates for teams. Team member candidates must be able to participate in the decision-making process; function in a team environment; be able to be cross-trained; work exactly to directions; and possess the basic hand skills necessary to do assembly work.

Ten

Beyond Kaizen

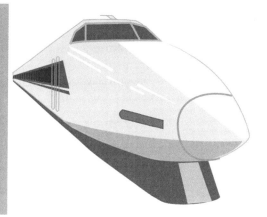

THE WORK SMART MANAGEMENT SYSTEM

Holistically, the Toyota Production System (TPS) has been proven to work in companies across many industries. But invariably, many companies have taken their own steps to "re-invent" it—picking and choosing certain concepts à la carte, which results in a less effective and disjointed version of TPS—one that will only deliver limited results.

To aid companies in the proper application of TPS, the author's Work Smart Management System (WSMS) provides a logical and simple approach. Many companies have found it easy to understand and administer because WSMS gives sequential remedies for what ails a non-lean company in three areas that are familiar to everyone. As shown in Figure 10-1, three pre-lean steps support management's deployment of lean across an organization: 1) development of a strategic plan, 2) development of the "culture structure," and 3) the execution phase where the policies of the "culture structure" and strategic plan become reality. Figure 10-2 provides a detailed breakdown of the WSMS, which shows the progressive steps a company must take to become a self-regulating, lean visual factory.

Lean Implementation Sequence

According to the Work Smart Management System, lean implementation occurs in the following sequence.

1. Learn about lean.

2. Gain management commitment.

Lean Deployment

Corporate Management	Operational Management	Shop Floor
Strategic plan	Culture structure	Execution
Assumptions	Organizational architecture	Toyota Production System 14 concepts
Budgets	Work Smart Management System	Work Smart Management System
Community	Information architecture	Hoshin kanri
Current conditions	Value stream maps	Seven basic tools
Customers	Rewards & recognition	Plan, do, check, act
Goals & objectives	Expertise	Quality at the source
Work Smart Management System	Responsibilities	Activity-based costing
Market analysis	Commitment	Pardigm shifts
Policy Development	**Policy Deployment**	**Policy Implementation**

Figure 10-1.

Work Smart Management System

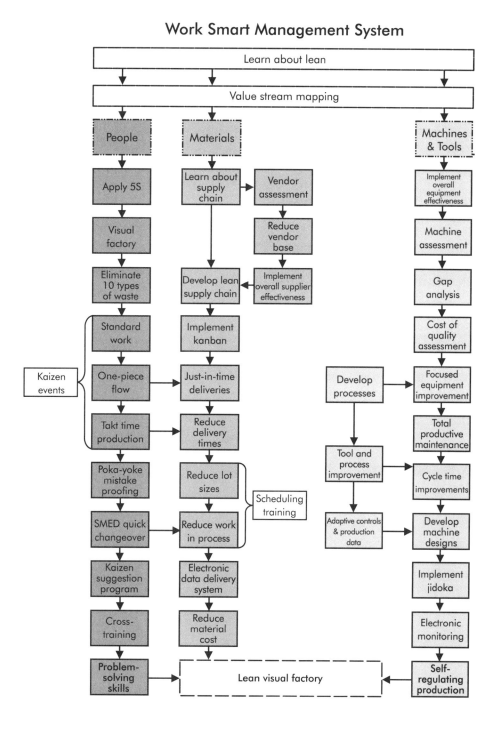

Figure 10-2.

3. Develop a strategic plan. The plan outlines goals, objectives, and required resources. A timeline is given along with cost and payback figures.

4. Determine the new lean metrics.

5. Develop the "culture structure."

6. Do an organizational assessment.

7. Determine product families using product-quantity analysis (discussed later in this chapter and in Chapter 7).

8. Draw a current-state value stream map (discussed later in this chapter and in Chapter 7).

9. Draw the future-state value stream map (discussed later in this chapter and in Chapter 7).

10. Create a kaizen proposal, including training needs.

11. Implement kaizen—do it to the plan!

12. Reassess the kaizen plan and adjust it to accommodate organizational needs. Compare it to the strategic plan's goals and objectives. Retrain and reinvest in capital, manpower, and technology.

1. *Learn About Lean.*

Most business executives have heard all the buzzwords describing new "flavor-of-the-month" improvement schemes. Many companies relegate these new methodologies to a small portion of the business, to be tried out, investigated, and to see, when thrown against the wall, what sticks. Lean is not a flavor-of-the-month, nor is it something that can be relegated to only a portion of the business. It means doing less and getting more. It is the methodology Toyota has perfected—the Toyota Production System. Lean is a philosophy based on worker participation and involvement in the decision-making process. The workers own the processes and are accountable for results.

There must be a paradigm shift in the way a business is run. This change, which represents 85% of the lean transformation, involves cultural change. Workers are taught the value of time, how to eliminate waste, about the sense of urgency, and importance of dedication and commitment. They become proactive in daily decision-making through participative management and teaming. Kaizen suggestion programs are put in place. Only after workers understand the thinking behind the philosophy can the remaining 15%, which involves physical transformation of processes, take place. Workers who co-author change will champion it. Everyone comes to know that getting "lean" is not a destination; it is a continuous journey to perfection.

On the lean journey there are many ways to fail, including:

- Lack of top-down management support and no strategic plan for lean implementation;

- Lack of middle management/ supervisor buy-in;

- Lack of communication;

- Not understanding that lean is all about people;

- Lack of customer focus;

- Lack of process improvement measures;

- Lack of dedicated and properly trained lean leadership;

- People measures are not aligned with lean goals and metrics;

- Using kaizen events as the sole improvement method and misusing six-sigma; and

- Performance-based pay systems where the only measure is company profitability.

Middle managers must realize that their job requirements have changed. Managers and supervisors now assume the roles of mentors, trainers, teachers, and consolers. They no longer tell workers what to do but instead offer the training and tools necessary for them to figure out what they need to do. The idea is to drive problem solving to the lowest level, closest to where they originate, so they can be resolved by the people most familiar with the everyday operation.

2. Gain management commitment.

Without 100% total commitment to lean transformation from upper management, lean will not succeed. Upper management must support it like the pig that gives us bacon for breakfast, not like the chicken that gives us the eggs. To gain upper management's support and commitment, they must first understand the psychological aspects of lean, which are key to its success.

For years manufacturers have created products in anticipation of having a market for them. Operations have been driven by sales forecasts and maximizing production efficiency at each level of the operation. Companies buffered inventories just in case there might be an upward fluctuation in demand.

Contrastingly, lean manufacturing—the Toyota Production System—is based on the premise that production can and should be driven by actual customer demand. Instead of pushing product through the factory and waiting for it to be sold, it is pulled through a system designed to be immediately responsive to the customer's needs. Lean organizations are able to produce quality products more economically, in lower volumes, quicker than the competition. Lean management is about running a business the most efficiently and economically way possible, thus maximizing return on investment.

World-class lean businesses know that lean is a corporate vision and an important element of the company's strategic plan, which affects everyone in the company. The lean philosophy requires a major paradigm shift in the way people think about business processes. It is all about eliminating waste from anywhere it my hide. Any action that does not add value in the eyes of the customer is waste. And lean

can be applied anywhere in the organization to eliminate waste and streamline processes, from the front office, to suppliers, to the support activities within a business. There is waste everywhere!

3. *Develop a Strategic Plan.*

A company's strategic plan outlines how it plans to attain goals and objectives relating to:

- Company priorities,

- Profit,

- Potentials for growth and acquisition, for example, new markets, etc.,

- Quality and cost of quality,

- Costs, such as labor, fringe benefits, material, facilities, etc.,

- Delivery,

- Assumptions about the economy, finance, taxes, raw materials, manpower, transportation and logistics, capacities, markets, regulations, machines and equipment, technology, expertise, etc.,

- Budgets and cash flow,

- Community,

- Current conditions,

- Customers, and the

- Work Smart Management System for lean implementation.

To develop the lean strategic plan, first there must be an understanding of the benefits of lean and its use for attaining the goals and objectives of the company. What is the company trying to achieve in the future, say 15 or 20 years from now? To achieve those goals, where does the company have to be next year, in 5 years, in 10 years? What is the operating plan to get there?

The operating plan will mandate developing the cultural side of lean, setting the policies for the entire organization. Policy development is then handed over to the operational management people where a culture structure is created, based upon the cultural and psychological aspects of lean. This becomes the policy deployment methodology, which is handed over to the workplace for execution.

4. Determine New Lean Metrics.

For lean to succeed there has to be a new set of operating rules and controls. The way progress is measured has to change to reflect new metrics, which guide the journey toward perfection.

The metrics by which a company measures itself relate to attaining the goals and objectives of the strategic plan. However, other metrics have to be included to measure and track progress, or lack of, in non-monetary areas, such as compliance to rules and regulations, safety issues, and some intangible areas such as kaizen suggestions submitted and adopted, cross-trained individuals, flexibility, and morale. The following metrics are based on quantifiable elements of the physical lean shop floor:

- Floor space used,

- Total part travel,

- Number of operators,

- Number of support personnel,

- Work in process,

- Units produced per labor/hour,

- Cost per piece,

- Manufacturing lead time,

- 5S rating,

- Value-added ratio, and

- Scrap rate (parts per million).

Additional metrics are used to measure lean progress:

- First-pass yield,

- Changeover reduction time,

- Overall equipment effectiveness (OEE),

- Downtime due to machine failure,

- Cost of maintenance per piece,

- Dock to dock time,

- Build to schedule,

- Number of kaizen suggestions submitted and implemented,

- Value of kaizen implementations,

- Number of injuries and accidents,

- Utility costs, and

- Worker absenteeism, including late start, and early leave.

5. Develop the "Culture Structure."

The "culture structure" involves the creation of the lean mindset that is necessary for it to be successful. It is the character of the system; the conscience of the team. The goals and objectives handed down from top management are achieved by the people in the organization through the application of the lean philosophy and tools.

Operational management is responsible for developing the culture structure, which becomes the plan for policy deployment. It is the methodology of changing the old paradigms of previous methodologies. Part of policy deployment is setting up the organizational architecture. This has to do with establishing employee classifications, company policies and procedures, rules and regulations, skill matrices, roles and responsibilities, and remuneration.

In the operating plan, what is culturally different is that most managers have not been exposed to a system kaizen, which is the overall flow path of how manufacturing and logistics are melded together so that the strategic plan can be obtained. New management skills must be developed. Workers now are part of a team and individuals are trained to make decisions at their working levels. They are trained on the tools and given permission to fix problems as they arise. Tools include the following:

- Histogram, which is a bar graph showing frequency data and the easiest way to evaluate the distribution of data and make visual comparisons.

- Pareto diagram, which is a bar graph used to identify and prioritize problems to be solved— actually it is a histogram aided by the 80/20 rule. (Approximately 80% of the problems are created by 20% of the causes.)

- Cause-and-effect diagram, also called the Ishikawa diagram or fishbone diagram, it is used to discover all the possible causes for a particular effect. The major purpose of this diagram is to act as a first step in problem solving by creating a list of possible causes. It allows the examination of worst-case scenarios.

- Run chart, which is used to analyze processes according to time or order to track variation.

- Scatter diagram, which is used to study and identify the possible relationship between the changes observed in two different sets of variables. For example, if the speed of the machine is increased, how many more parts will it make?

- Flow chart, which is a pictorial representation showing all of the steps in a process. There are many variations to this chart. One type shows information flow and is used extensively with computer programs to show process sequence.

- Control chart, which is used to determine whether a process will produce a service or product with consistent measurable properties. It allows a process to be reviewed to see if it is within acceptable tolerances. Thus it is used extensively as a quality reporting chart, especially with statistical process control (SPC).

Development of the culture structure also is reliant on having the correct computer and operating system, one geared up to track the lean initiatives as well as the other metrics necessary to operate the business.

6. Do an Organizational Assessment.

Businesses are comprised of three major elements: 1) the people who run the business and perform the actions that satisfy the customer, 2) the materials used to either build components for the customer or those necessary to do the tasks used to satisfy the customer, and 3) tools and machines that aid the processes of the business, including those that transform raw materials into finished goods, the computers that coordinate processes and materials and keep track of inventories, and others such as copy machines, telephones, and office equipment.

The organizational assessment looks at a company's usage of these elements from a lean perspective and then benchmarks them against Toyota.

To perform the assessment, choose two or three of the most important elements that align with the goals and objectives of the strategic plan from each of the following categories: people, materials, and tools and machines. Using Figure 10-3, follow the incremental scoring of each criterion that applies to "people" to determine the company's level of leanness and what will need to improve to achieve the goals and objectives of the organization. These elements then become the first areas to improve. The Work Smart Management System (see Figures 10-1 and 10-2) is then referred to for the list of improvement activities. The same process is followed for material (see Figure 10-4) and then tools and machines (see Figure 10-5).

7. Determine Product Families.

The next step is to determine the product family that will be targeted.

This is done with successive Pareto analyses and Product Quantity Charts. (See Chapter 7 for examples.) Product family analysis determines what process a cell should contain to handle the parts that require the same processes. The more familial parts run through a cell, the more flexibility.

8. Draw a Current-state Value Stream Map.

A current state value stream map is drawn to show the entire set of activities (value adding and otherwise) running from raw material to finished product for a specific product (or in some cases, product family). The flow of data and information is as critical as the flow of material in production. All engineering functions need to be mapped. This will show the flow of designs and drawings as well as the bottlenecks encountered and the individual elemental process times. An example of a current-state value stream map is shown in Figure 10-6.

9. Draw a Future-state Value Stream Map.

Figure 10-7 highlights kaizen opportunities that will improve the process flow that was shown in Figure

Pillar	Criterion	0	1	2	3	4	5	Score
People	5S	Impossible for outsiders to determine what is happening anywhere. Dirty conditions.	Floor dirty, benches disorganized, WIP everywhere. No communication.	Plant uses floor lines and labeling. Material not organized. Some bulletin boards used.	Clean floors with lines. Material identified clearly & stored. Bulletin boards well used.	Proactive approach to orderliness & cleanliness. Regular 5S activities monitored.	Every area of facility is as clean and orderly as possible. Regular posting of 5S scores.	
	Elimination of waste	Waste obvious everywhere. No conservation evident anywhere.	Beginning plant-wide program to eliminate waste. Some lead employees trained.	Some evidence of improvements. Progress tracked and posted. 2nd level employees trained.	Tracking waste savings and posting results. Company-wide awareness of waste.	Substantial $ savings. 3rd level of employees trained. Savings tracked and posted.	No waste visible. Substantial accumulated $ savings. Savings postings are constant.	
	Kaizen suggestions	"Kaizen" is a foreign word not spoken here.	Few ideas used sparingly. No improvement tracking. No formal suggestion program.	Employees encouraged to submit ideas. No formal kaizen program. Implementation spotty.	Formal kaizen suggestion program in place. Implementation and savings tracked.	Formal kaizen suggestion program with full-time administrator. Significant savings.	Suggestion program fully operational. Average of 35 suggestions submitted per person.	
	Takt time production	Batch & queue. Always late. Excessive $ tied up in WIP. Schedules are always wrong.	Batch & queue. Excessive $ tied up in WIP. Many schedule interruptions to process hot jobs.	Production run to monthly schedule with weekly adjustment. 75% on-time. Excessive WIP.	Production run to weekly schedule with minimum changes. Small lots and reduced WIP.	Schedule planned by customers' actual requirements. Takt time achieved 75% of time.	Takt time is in the scheduling mechanism. Consistent track record of on-time delivery.	
	Pull system	Push system. Inventory scattered all over the shop. Constantly missing delivery dates.	Push system with organized storage sites. Works to master production schedule.	Push system with triggers. Material released from floor storage for production.	Kanban used in some production. Lot sizes reduced. Schedule adjusted daily.	Kanban used extensively. Lot sizes allow production to takt time. No excess WIP.	Complete shop run with kanban, one piece at a time. Extensive SMED. No extra material.	
	Single-minute exchange of dies (SMED)	Changeovers take >12 hours and require extensive adjustments when complete.	Changeovers take <12 hours and require extensive adjustments when complete.	Changeovers take 4-6 hours and require extensive adjustments before production.	Changeovers done in <4 hours. Minimal adjustments needed, quality good.	Changeovers done in <30 minutes. Minimal adjustments needed for production.	Changeovers done in <10 minutes. No adjustments required in production.	
	Poka-yoke	No preventive measures to eliminate making defective parts.	No program to address errors in the workplace. Left up to the operators to make good parts.	Error prevention used throughout shop. Each operator on their own.	Formal training in poka-yoke for key personnel. Errors tracked and costed. Good results.	All operators trained in error elimination. Errors tracked and costed. Significant progress.	Poka-yoke program mature. Now a way of life. All new parts designed for poka-yoke.	
	Standardization	No standardization of anything–process, training, machinery, or tooling.	Standardization of some tools & machines. Some family of parts process grouping.	Tools & machines standardized. Production process up to the discretion of operator.	Company policy to standardize. Standard Work Combination Sheets used.	All operators work to Standard Work Combination Sheets. All sheets posted.	Everything in shop standardized–processes, training, and reporting. Lean culture in place.	
	Autonomation (jidoka)	All processes geared to high production. No understanding of "man and machine" concept.	Processes geared to large lots and minimal automation use. Manual operations separate.	Automation used throughout plant but not optimized.	Machines can make bad parts. Manual tasks apart from machine. Operator runs 1 machine.	Machine stops when bad part is made. Operator runs several machines. Poka-yoke used.	Operator runs cell. No bad parts made. Machine adjusts itself. Automatic load/unload.	
	Teaming	No teaming. All workers work by themselves. No cross-training. No multiple tasks.	Temporary teams formed for manual operations. No formal team training-up to supervisor.	Teaming used by choice of supervisor. Minimal training of workers and management.	Company policy to use teams as needed. No formal program company wide.	Company policy to use teams extensively. Formal training prior to implementation.	100% use of teams company policy. Formal training. Now way of life–cultural acceptance.	
	Employee value	Employees used as needed. No training. No voice in daily operations. Do as you are told.	Dictatorial environment. High absenteeism and turnover. Morale low. No future here on this job!	Management tries to improve worker skills with minimal training. Use of worker skills minimal.	Needs assessed. Training to augment skills. Employees have voice in training.	Specific skill needs met in all areas. Open dialogue with workers. Skills matrix used.	Employees completely cross-trained. Know and use all TPS tools. Skills matrix complete.	
	Safety	Numerous lost-time accidents per year. OSHA violations evident. Dangerous place.	Occasional lost-time accidents. No formal safety awareness program in operation.	No major lost-time accidents but still many cuts and bruises. No awareness program.	Fairly safe workplace. Company safety policy. Proactive accident prevention policy.	All employees have attended safety training and practice safe work habits.	Accident-free for at least 6 months.	
							Subtotal	
							Subtotal × 1.67 = %	

Figure 10-3.

Pillar	Criterion	0	1	2	3	4	5	Score
Material	Supply chain	Too many suppliers, no real relationships. Buy on price and delivery only.	Minimal standards for suppliers. Rated on cost, delivery, & quality, but price is most important.	Fewer suppliers used. Some partnering. Use quality, cost, and delivery grading system.	Long-term partnerships with some suppliers. Plans to improve quality, cost, & delivery.	Long-term partnerships in place. Improving quality, cost & delivery.	Selected suppliers automatically reduce prices, improve quality and delivery.	
	WIP standard	Excess material at each workstation. Do not know amount of WIP or its $ value.	Push system. WIP controlled and schedule driven by MRP. Run until material is gone.	MRP drives push system. Lot sizes determined by MRP and changeover times.	Pull system, MRP not driver. Lot sizes determined by takt time. Changeover problems.	Lot sizes small, scheduled by takt time. Changeovers < 30 minutes, WIP within 10%.	One-piece flow production to takt time. No excess inventory. SMED <10 minutes.	
	Kanban	No kanban. All material in large batches all around workplace. Inventory count needed.	Material quantities only known by doing an inventory based on MRP Schedule by MRP.	Some kanban training. Some cells with kanban. No Water Spiders. Still push system.	Kanban used throughout shop. Shop floor trained in kanban use. Water Spider used.	Kanban used 100% in production and some with suppliers. Water Spiders used.	100% kanban operation, including suppliers. > 6 months kanban in use.	
	Just-in-time delivery	Never in time.	On schedule by luck, not by plan. Constant interruptions to facilitate rush orders.	Constant schedule juggling due to hot rush jobs that are late. >50% of jobs are late.	>75% on-time delivery. Still many interruptions for late orders. Poor efficiency.	>90% on-time delivery. Changeovers <10 minutes. Adherence to schedule.	All schedules met 100% of time for 6 months. No excess inventory. Work to takt time.	
	One-piece flow	Work done in batches & determined by material on hand and resource availability.	Work done in batches & determined by resource availability and customer priorities.	Smaller batches, better schedule, excess WIP. Process-based production not by product.	Cells used extensively with multiple operators. Minimal WIP. <100% to takt time.	Cells run by 1 operator where possible. WIP at minimum. Daily working to takt time with overtime	6 months running to takt time with no equalization needed. Cells run by 1 operator as designed.	
	Supplier quality	Quality suspect. Supplier does not check each piece. Get credit for scrap material only.	Low level of quality. No 100% inspections on materials. Quality level not improving.	Quality improving. Indications of supplier process improvement.	Quality improving. Supplier is working with company to make improvements. 3 sigma.	Supplier has quality improvement plan in operation. Results are good. 4 sigma.	Supplier consistently provides material better than 5 sigma. 6-month acceptable record.	
	Supplier atmosphere	Not right atmosphere for kaizen implementation. No intercompany kanban. No improvement plans.	Not using kanban fully. Plan needs to be made for implementation. Forming liaison team.	Beginning in-plant training on kanban. People assigned. First attempt at just-in-time.	Working with supplier to cross-train each other's workers. Definite commitment to JIT.	Shared resources. Continuous JIT improvement. Savings for supplier & company.	6 months continuous utilization of co-shared improvement plan. Both companies benefiting.	
	Supplier performance	On-time delivery 60% of time. Numerous delivery promise dates not kept.	On-time delivery 70%. Promised delivery dates routinely missed. Fair response to stock-outs.	On-time delivery 80%. Fewer stock-outs. Vendor improving on-time delivery.	On-time delivery 90%. Stock-outs almost never happen. Fairly quick replenishment.	On-time delivery 100%. No stock-outs. Supplier improving, has plan in place.	On-time delivery 100%. Fully implemented improvement plan. 6-month record.	
	Design for manufacturability	Manual design, no CAD. No design for manufacturability. No concurrent engineering.	Computer used, some CAD/CAM but not company policy. No design software used.	Design review meetings encouraged to feed back to designers. Concurrent engineering	Most design criteria on computer database. All designs CAD/CAM. Costing a criterion.	All designs created from stored data. Least cost manufacturing principles routinely applied.	New designs consider accumulated data on least cost manufacturing. 6-month success record.	
	Supplier costing	Heavy pricing & delivery constraints. Unable to reduce costs. High quality costs. Profits eroding.	Contentious improvement attempts. Price reduction pressure. Some cost improvements	Few target cost improvements. Some limited kaizen cost improvements.	Showing continuous improvement in reducing costs. Good kaizen costing results.	Sustained continuous costing improvements by targeted and kaizen costing means.	6-month record of sustained cost improvements with high quality and delivery.	
	Environmental impact	No money allocated to prevent pollution. Obvious violations of environmental laws.	No money allocated to prevent pollution. Obvious violations of environmental laws.	Minimal effort to not pollute. No money allocated to fight pollution. Passive effort.	Definite program to actively fight pollution. Compliant with all regulations.	Education of all employees as to the importance of not polluting.	6-month history of perfect compliance with all regulations, with no exceptions or citations.	
	Supplier development	Supplier not enrolled in an improvement plan. Lacks resources to commit to a program.	Looking around for different plans and programs. Will commit later when affordable.	Beginning development plan. Initial training complete. Program launched.	Ongoing training. Implementation at key operations. Limited good results.	All employees trained. Program running and fruitful. Shared gains with end user.	6 months of efficient implementation. Gains plentiful and consistent. Top-rated supplier.	

Subtotal

Subtotal × 1.67 = %

Figure 10-4.

Pillar	Criterion	0	1	2	3	4	5	Score
Tools & Machines	Process design	Because of a lack of resources, best processes sometimes not utilized.	No quality function deployment (QFD) or target costing. No tool & process engineering.	Target costs usually met. Equipment designed for speed, not flexibility. TPM not practiced.	QFD good. No SMED. Cost & delivery targets usually met. Control of manufacturing costs.	New products introduced on time and at cost, with good quality. Minimal startup.	Target costs routinely beaten. Company-wide cost reduction program up and working.	
	Cost	Costs vary from order to order. No long-term contracts. Costs unpredictable.	Costs based on contracts with rising costs. No measure undertaken to reduce costs.	Costs based on annual contracts with clauses that stipulate cost reductions.	Plan co-authored by supplier and company to mutually reduce costs is in place & functional.	All costs known and controlled. Regular plan to continuously reduce costs in operation.	6 months continuous control of costs with regular cost reductions as a result.	
	Quality	Lowest quality standard. Very problematic. Continuous fight over acceptable material.	Minimum quality standard. All shipments must be 100% inspected. Processes poor.	Processes yield errors and rejects. Physical inspections necessary. No poka-yoke used.	Poka-yokes used throughout plant. Processes somewhat sound. Good quality.	Errors and defects controlled. Processes will not allow bad material to be used.	6 months continuous supply of 100% acceptable material. Poka-yokes used.	
	Total productive maintenance (TPM)	Equipment repaired after breakdowns. Much production time lost due to repairs.	No autonomous maintenance. Equipment repair after breakdowns. Production time lost.	Using autonomous maintenance in a few places. Workers not trained on TPM.	Autonomous maintenance training complete. Most operators doing TPM.	Autonomous maintenance concept fully embraced. Machine downtime reduced.	6 months of complete TPM program. No lost production time. Quality improved.	
	Documentation	Paperwork consists of a sheet of paper with minimal instructions. No computers used.	Minimal computer use. Process sheets or routers used. Paperwork always behind production.	Some Standard Work Combination Sheets in cells, posted weekly after production is run.	Use of Standard Work Combination Sheets in all places & posted daily. Improvements tracked.	Standard Work Combination Sheets understood & used by all. Computer generated.	6 months history of use and posting at every workstation and bulletin board plant wide.	
	Skills development	None.	Training by watching other person for a while. No standardized format or procedure.	Skills matrix developed but not updated or complete. Recognized skills training program.	Skills matrix accurate & up to date. Ongoing training programs. Outside training.	Tuition reimbursement used for college courses and related training well received by many.	People's skills are the company's best asset, commanding more pay, recognition, & benefits.	
	Process validation	No process validation.	Process validation on startup of new process only. No continuous validations.	Validations come routinely with supplier input. Processes checked as quality declines.	All validations available. Processes continuously checked & matched against validation.	Computer-controlled validation record and monitoring of all processes.	Mature system of computer designing validation parameters based on past data.	
	Machine condition	Machine conditions poor at best. No method of knowing existing condition or status.	Machines are a mix of old & new. No proactive TPM system to maintain good condition.	Machines periodically adjusted & repaired. Quality fluctuates due to machine conditions.	Machines regularly maintained & adjusted to specifications. Minimal scrap.	Machines continually adjusted and improved, better than new. No scrap.	6 months of production with no downtime due to breakdowns or making scrap.	
	Pre-production planning (3P)	No pre-production planning.	Processes not mature, vary from day to day. Many adjustments needed. Scrap problem.	Cellular manufacturing with outputs ≤ 75%. Cells manually adjusted frequently.	Cellular manufacturing with poka-yoke & TPM. Outputs ≤ 85%. Few quality problems.	Cellular manufacturing with poka-yoke & TPM. No scrap or WIP. Run to takt time daily.	6-month history of no scrap, running to takt time, and no problems. Process in total control.	
	Product evolution	How to ramp-up production & not make scrap is not understood. Speed over-emphasized.	Commercialization begins, slow ramp-up. Poor documentation & training. No planning.	Ramp-up improves but documentation & training lagging. Material availability problems.	Ramp-up well planned. Training done prior to startup. Full production in <2 weeks.	All startups done on schedule as planned. Full production <1 week. No flow problems.	6-month history of successful launches on time and at quality level expected.	
	Technical risk management	Risk assessment not done.	Risks analyzed after the fact by untrained personnel. No compiled database for later use.	Risk management used in its simplest form to react to quality, cost, and delivery problems.	Risk management used before production begins to evaluate all possible scenarios.	Risk management treated as a business process & applied where needed. Scorecard.	Risk scorecards used proactively to assess & improve technical, cost, and schedule risks.	
	Overall equipment effectiveness (OEE)	No form of continual machine evaluation.	Machines utilized by past performance/availability. No loads based on efficiency or output cap.	Minimal records kept on machine efficiency, speed and quality. Schedule not driven by performance.	OEE recognized and used in some areas. Operators trained in its use and importance.	OEE >75% and consistently improving. All operators trained and participate.	OEE >80% for 6 months.	
							Subtotal	
							Subtotal × 1.67 = %	

Figure 10-5.

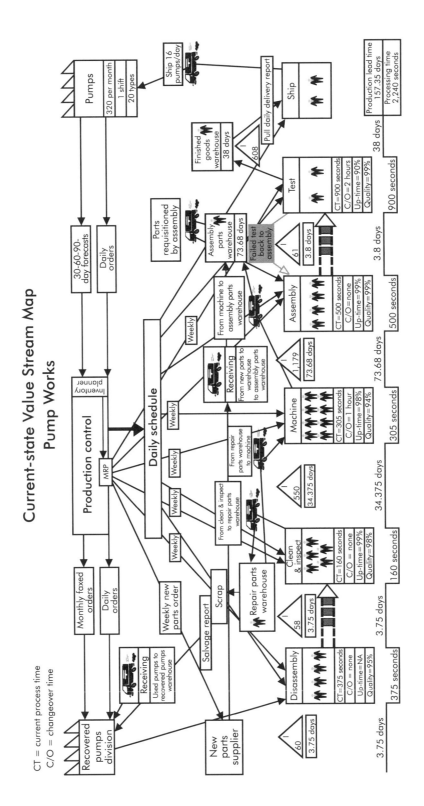

Figure 10-6.

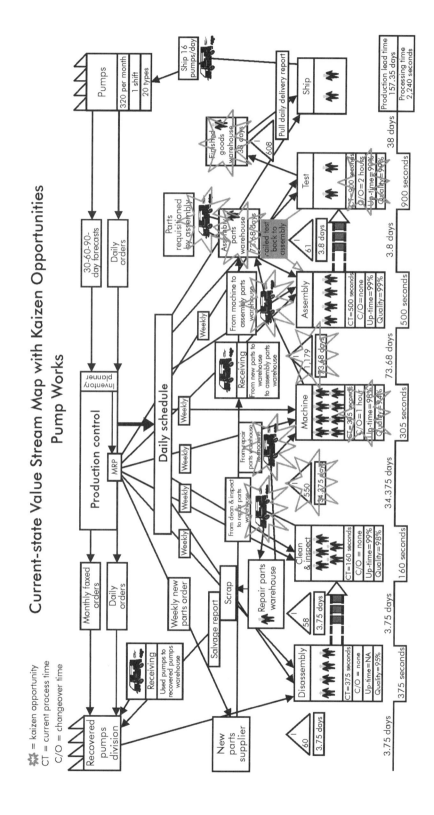

Figure 10-7.

10-6. However, the ultimate future state map, one with all non-value-added activities removed, is shown in Figure 10-8. The new layout for the process is shown in Figure 10-9.

10. Create a Kaizen Proposal.

To achieve the new lean layout will require making the changes indicated in the future-state value stream map. The method to get there will take the form of kaizen event(s). The proposal for kaizen implementation is documented, detailing the event schedule, training, and follow-up activities. Targeted areas include those that appear on the value stream map (Figure 10-7) or bottlenecks where specific improvements will allow achievement of the goals and objectives of the strategic plan. Following are considerations for selecting the kaizen area(s):

- It is guaranteed to succeed.

- It is visual.

- It is a complete product, not a process.

- The methodology can be copied and used in other areas.

- It will make a significant impact to a bottleneck or production restriction.

- Improvements will have a significant market or financial impact.

- Choose operational problems—not management or policy issues.

- It has a sound initial process in place.

- Select a product that can be made in a cell with fewer than 12 operators.

- Select a product that is medium-to-high volume.

- Select areas that were highlighted in Figure 10-7.

- Select areas that have relatively good overall equipment effectiveness (OEE).

- Refer back to the organizational assessment results to see critical areas for improvement.

11. Implement Kaizen.

Kaizen roll-out and implementation should follow the plan. It is a good idea to chart all of the kaizen events on a master Gantt chart showing all the tasks, their duration, and the resources needed. Using available software, such as Microsoft Project®, facilitates tracking, quick updating, and broadcasting status to everyone involved.

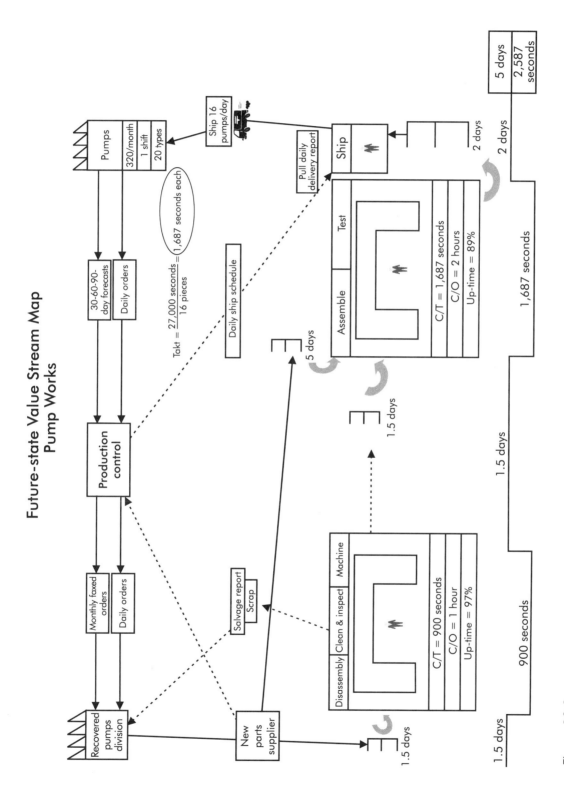

Future-state Value Stream Map
Pump Works

Figure 10-8.

New Lean Layout

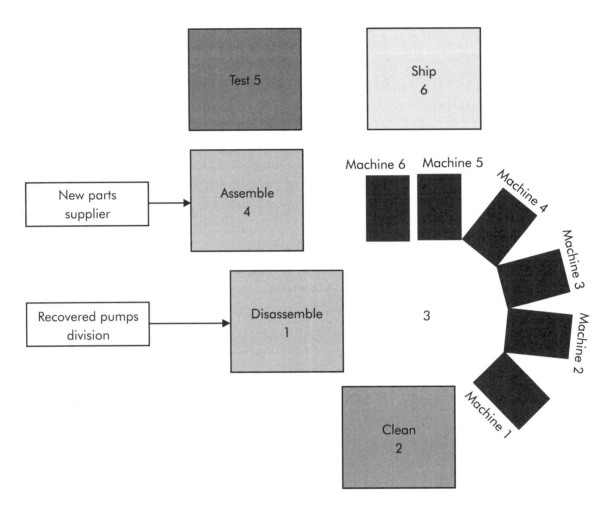

Figure 10-9.

12. *Reassess the Kaizen Plan.*

Periodic reviews of the kaizen plan are integral to successful lean implementation. To minimize regression there needs to be constant attention paid to the metrics used to measure production as well as continuous improvement.

The plan is adjusted according to what the metrics are reporting so alignment with the goals and objectives of the strategic plan is maintained.

THE PARALLEL TOOLS OF LEAN

Kaizen is continuous improvement; thus it never really ends. However, there are other complementary lean tools, which when used in parallel with kaizen events, strengthen a company even more. World-class companies have many of the tools discussed here in their repertoires.

Total Productive Maintenance

One of the most important tools is *total productive maintenance* (TPM). Its definition embodies all the methods used to maintain machines and equipment. By practicing TPM, a company is ensured that machines and equipment are always able to perform to the required production levels without unexpected interruptions or reduced output levels.

With TPM, operators assume responsibility for certain portions of the maintenance of equipment. By servicing machines and equipment at regular intervals and tracking every hour of production, small problems are alleviated before they become larger. And more comprehensive maintenance, such as the modification of machines to allow for easier adjustments or improvements to function, is scheduled for when it is convenient for downtime to occur.

Overall Equipment Effectiveness

TPM uses overall equipment effectiveness (OEE) as a benchmark or a measure of a machine's efficiency to determine the effect of improvements. It is calculated as follows (Bakerjian 1993):

$$O_E = M_A \times M_P \times Q_R \qquad \text{(Eq. 10-1)}$$

where:

O_E = overall equipment effectiveness, %

M_A = machine or equipment availability, %

M_P = machine or equipment performance rate, %

Q_R = quality rate, %

Machine availability (M_A) is calculated as:

$$M_A = \frac{A_R - D_A}{A_R} \qquad \text{(Eq. 10-2)}$$

where:

A_R = required availability to meet production requirements (minutes or hours)

D_A = downtime (including scheduled maintenance, unscheduled downtime, setups, etc.)

The machine or equipment performance rate (M_P) is calculated as:

$$M_P = \frac{C_T \times M_O}{O_T} \qquad \text{(Eq. 10-3)}$$

where:

C_T = ideal cycle time (parts per hour)

M_O = machine or equipment output (total parts in the given time period)

O_T = operating time (hours, minutes) = M_A

The quality rate (Q_R) is calculated as:

$$Q_R = \frac{P_I - P_D}{P_I} \qquad \text{(Eq. 10-4)}$$

where:

P_I = number of pieces input to the process

P_D = number of pieces output as defective from the process

The goal for overall equipment effectiveness is 85% or greater.

Total Quality Management

Total quality management (TQM) is a comprehensive and structured approach to organizational management that seeks to improve the quality of products and services through ongoing refinements in response to continuous feedback from customers. This is done by eliminating the non-value-added activities, duplicate tasks, and wasted effort of employees. For example, a process may use two persons where only one is sufficient to perform a task.

In general, TQM is concerned only with managerial and engineering employees (salaried, exempt)—in other words, positions that are not paid hourly. In practice, TQM promotes the "leaning" of management in an organization.

TQM seeks to:

- Assign the right person to do the right task, achieve the asked for results, and only do it once.

- Eliminate waste and unproductive activities.

- Establish the priorities of each individual and standardize the execution of tasks.

Hoshin Planning

Hoshin planning (also called hoshin kanri or policy deployment) is a high-level management tool, generally used for strategic planning within a company.

In practice, hoshin planning unifies and aligns resources while establishing clear metrics, by which progress toward key objectives can be measured on a regular basis. There are usually three to five key metrics that are tracked, indicating progress toward goals.

The use of hoshin planning provides focus for a company. It forces management to establish and track priorities. At times, this may even mean placing some projects and activities on hold while projects with higher priorities take precedence.

Primarily, there are seven tools used in hoshin planning:

1. Histograms
2. Cause-and-effect diagrams
3. Check sheets
4. Pareto diagrams
5. Graphs
6. Control charts
7. Scatter diagrams

Quality Function Deployment

Quality function deployment (QFD), also known as concurrent engineering, is a policy that allows for decisions to be made by multi-skilled teams who possess a common understanding of customer needs and how to best satisfy them. It is a way to concurrently resolve problems confronting the many functions involved in the design and manufacture of products.

QFD also looks at the development of best practices. And it is concerned with reducing costs while improving the product. QFD is especially helpful in reducing the time needed to launch a new product.

Value Stream Mapping

A value stream map is a blueprint for lean implementation. A value stream represents all the sequences required to bring a product through the main flows essential to every product, from raw material to finished goods. What makes a value stream map different than a process map is it shows the information flow along with the process flow. It offers a strategic high-level view of the complete factory and all the inert processes that constitute making finished products.

The importance of value stream mapping (VSM) is it visualizes the steps necessary to produce finished goods. A person does not have to be an engineer or management expert to understand the flow. Simple stick figure drawings are used to clearly show the steps.

A value stream map clearly identifies waste in a company at all levels. It shows the flow of product and all the delays encountered. It ties together the whole plant operation, making it an invaluable tool to use before a kaizen event. The value stream map forms the basis of the improvement plan by revealing the entire manufacturing cycle from beginning to end.

Business Process Reengineering

Business process reengineering (BPR) takes a management approach to problem solving. It recommends certain prescribed methods and techniques for redesigning operational processes so they better reflect the core competency of the business and address customer-oriented concerns.

BPR has been called process innovation—by rethinking and redesigning business processes, sharp improvements in performance can result. Time is spent implementing ideas that are "out of the box," as opposed to wasting time making improvements to an antiquated system that will never produce quantum results. Using a fresh approach, BPR takes what has always been done and optimizes the tasks so they are done in the best ways possible.

The goals, processes, and outcomes of BPR have their roots in various well-known organizational efficiency, productivity, and competitiveness movements. Lean manufacturing, specifically the Toyota Production System (TPS), is an example of reengineering taken to the ultimate level of improvement. BPR combines certain facets of TQM and TPS. However, its methods concentrate on the management level as opposed to targeting the shop floor first.

Six Sigma

Six sigma is a statistical way of measuring quality. It is not an inspection criterion; no inspection system on its own yields such excellent results. As an analytical tool, six sigma relies on data to detect problems. The actual "number" that six sigma represents is 3.4 defects per million units of output. This is the current goal of most manufacturers.

Where lean focuses on the elimination of waste, six sigma focuses on process variation. It uses the define, measure, analyze, improve, and control (DMAIC) method to resolve process variation. By understanding the critical few inputs to a process, it will produce controllable outputs, which in turn leads to fewer errors and mistakes and less scrap.

Usually a "Black Belt" or person who specializes in six sigma is assigned to a problem area to determine why there is not six-sigma quality and how the process can be improved. Typically, the Black Belt analyzes what is thought to be the source of errors or rejects to find the root cause. Second-level Pareto analyses are used, as well as design of experiments (DOE) and failure mode effects analysis (FMEA). The Black Belt then devises a solution to get the process to six-sigma quality by implementing the improvements. The process is then

monitored and the parts-per-million scrap rate is plotted. The project ends when the quality level is at 3.4 rejected parts per million or fewer.

The major drawback of solely applying six sigma, or any other lean tool in isolation, is that the regression rate is high. Once the project manager leaves, the process reverts back to the way it originally operated. The reason is the culture of the organization has not changed. Lean has not been instilled as a way of thinking, and thus the reason for maintaining six-sigma quality is not understood.

100% Quality

In the past, it was assumed that a certain amount of error could be expected and was acceptable from any operation. But what if everything was 99.9% good? How many airplanes would crash? Would you knowingly board a flight that was part of the 0.1%? Or, suppose hospital workers dropped 0.1% of all babies born in the delivery room. Would you want that 0.1% to include your newborn? In these instances, even 99.99% is not good enough. Some things must have better than six-sigma quality—anything less than 100% safe is unacceptable.

The ability exists now to design processes so that 100% of the output is good. The Toyota Production System is that method.

Product Quantity Analysis

Product quantity analysis (PQA) is a necessary tool used in the course of conducting kaizen events. It looks at the relationship between products and the quantity of products. PQA groups parts into families for process comparison purposes. It helps determine the flow of quantity and flow of product models.

To begin, PQA requires gathering several months' worth of data. A Pareto chart is constructed to organize and analyze the data so the ratios of parts to their volumes can be found. The highest volume will be at the top of the list, which declines to the least amount at the bottom. A PQA table is created where the vertical axis is the production output (quantity) and the horizontal axis shows the products (part numbers).

Using the 80-20 rule, the 20% of parts that represent 80% of the volume are selected. Next, each part is grouped according to its process steps. All the part numbers that require identical processes belong in the same group. As many groups as necessary are made to capture 80% of the volume. The group with the most volume will be designated group "A," the next most highest volume group, "B," etc. This continues until all the part numbers are in groups. Usually not more than four or five groups are needed. Grouping parts in such a way is also known as *group technology*. This method is used to determine the specific parts that will be made in a particular cell. Thus, new cells can be designed for maximum efficiency and return on investment.

REFERENCE

Bakerjian, Ramon, ed. 1993. *Tool and Manufacturing Engineers Handbook*, 4th Ed., Volume 7, *Continuous Improvement*. Chapter 15, "Total Productive Maintenance." (Dearborn, MI: Society of Manufacturing Engineers).

Appendix A

The Milestones of Lean

1760 Jean Radolphe Perronet, manufacturer of pins, produces first known record of work standards and time study.

1792 Thomas Mason, Old Derby China works, uses work standards to run production schedule.

1878 Frederick W. Taylor joins Midvale Steel Company.

1879 Albert Einstein and union organizer, Joe Hill, are born.

1880 American Society of Mechanical Engineers is founded.

Thomas Edison patents the incandescent light.

1881 Society of the Chemical Industry is founded in London.

Alexander Graham Bell publishes *Science* magazine.

1883 Frederick W. Taylor begins time studies at Midvale Steel Company.

1884 World Industrial and Cotton Exposition is held in New Orleans.

1885 Frank B. Gilbreth begins motion studies.

1886 Henry R. Towne publishes "The Engineer as Economist."

American Federation of Labor is organized.

1887 Interstate Commerce Commission is formed.

1890 Sherman Anti-trust Act becomes law in the US.

1891 Thomas Edison seeks a patent on motion pictures with film invented by George Eastman.

1892 Frank B. Gilbreth studies the motions of bricklayers.

1893 Frederick W. Taylor begins work as an engineer.

1895 Duryea Motor Wagon Company is founded—first automobile company in the US to produce gas-powered cars.

1896 Frederick W. Taylor publishes *A Piece Rate System*.

Thomas Edison invents the fluoroscope and releases it into the public domain without patenting it—"It's for all mankind."

1897 J. J. Thomson discovers electrons.

1898 Frederick W. Taylor begins work at Bethlehem Steel Company.

1899 Carl G. Barth invents the slide rule.

1901 National Bureau of Standards is established.

1902 Wright Brothers' conquer the sky with their first airplane flight.

1903 Frederick W. Taylor presents "Shop Management."

Henry Ford produces the first "Model A" car.

1904 Harrington Emerson implements Santa Fe Railroad improvement.

Thorstein Veblen publishes *The Theory of Business Enterprise.*

1905 Albert Einstein develops the "Theory of Relativity."

1906 Frederick W. Taylor establishes metal-cutting parameters.

1907 Frank B. Gilbreth applies time study in the construction industry.

1908 Henry Ford produces the "Model T" with interchangeable parts.

1909 Guglielmo Marconi is awarded the Nobel Prize in Physics for his invention of the "wireless."

1910 Henry L. Gantt establishes the Gantt Award Program.

Hugo Diemers publishes *Factory Organization and Administration.*

1911 Frederick W. Taylor publishes *The Principles of Scientific Management.*

1912   Harrington Emerson publishes *The Twelve Principles of Efficiency*.

Frank and Lillian Gilbreth publicize their concept of "therbligs" in *Principles of Scientific Management*, translated into Japanese.

1913   Henry Ford implements the moving assembly line.

1914   Clarence B. Thompson edits *Scientific Management*, a collection of Frederick W. Taylor's works.

Lillian Gilbreth publishes *The Psychology of Management*.

1915   Frederick W. Taylor's system is in use at Niigata's Kamata plant in Japan.

World War I begins in Europe.

Robert Hoxie publishes *Scientific Management and Labor*.

1916   Frederick W. Taylor Society is established in the US.

1917   Japan enacts "Factory Laws."

Henry L. Gantt develops the Gantt chart.

Frank and Lillian Gilbreth publish *Applied Motion Study*.

1918   Mary P. Follet publishes *The New State: Group Organization, the Solution of Popular Government*.

1919   Henry L. Gantt publishes "Organization for Work."

Frank and Lillian Gilbreth author "Therbligs and the 14 Descriptions."

1920   Merick Hathaway publishes "Time Study as a Basis for Rate Setting."

1921   Frank and Lillian Gilbreth introduce process analysis symbols to the American Society of Mechanical Engineers (ASME).

Albert Einstein wins the Nobel Prize in Physics.

1922   Washington Naval Limitation Treaty signed.

George S. Radford publishes *The Control of Quality in Manufacturing*.

Sakiichi Toyoda invents the automatic loom.

1923   Alfred Sloan becomes president of General Motors.

1924 Elton Mayo conducts illumination experiments.

Frank and Lillian Gilbreth publish the results of their "therbligs" micromotion work.

1925 Pratt & Whitney begin aircraft engine business.

Toshiro Ikeda translates Frederick W. Taylor's *Secrets of Eliminating Unprofitable Efforts* into Japanese.

1926 Henry Ford begins building "trimotor" airplanes.

1927 Elton Mayo tests at Hawthorne in the assembly room.

Henry Ford opens the Rouge Plant in Dearborn, Michigan.

1928 Chrysler starts Desoto and Plymouth manufacture.

1929 Kiichiro Toyoda visits Ford's Rouge Plant.

Great Depression begins.

1930 Dr. W. A. Shewhart develops the statistical process control (SPC) chart.

Merick Hathaway publishes "Machining and Standard Times."

Allan H. Mogensen publishes "Work Simplification."

1932 American automobile production is lowest since 1918.

Taiichi Ohno joins Toyoda.

American Society of Tool and Manufacturing Engineers (ASTME) is founded.

1933 Hitler becomes Chancellor of Germany.

Great Depression is at its worst.

1934 General Electric performs micromotion studies.

1935 Wagner Act is adopted in US, allowing unions in industry.

1936 World's first television broadcast occurs in Great Britain.

1937 Ralph M. Barnes publishes *Motion and Time Study*.

Toyota Motor Company is founded.

1938 Civil Aeronautics Act is passed—instituting the regulation of air traffic and fares.

1939 Ernest Lawrence invents the cyclotron.

1940 President Roosevelt cuts off supply of steel and oil to Japan and orders Japan to withdraw from China.

1941 R. L. Morrow publishes "Ratio Delay Study."

Fritz J. Roethlisberger publishes *Management and Morale*.

1942 Philip Murray becomes president of the United Steelworkers of America union.

1943 American Society of Mechanical Engineers (ASME) publishes standards and a glossary of terms.

1945 Marvin E. Mundel devises "Memo-motion Study."

Joseph H. Quick devises "Work Factor Methods."

Shigeo Shingo presents "Production as a Network of Processes" and explains lot delays to the Japanese Management Association (JMA).

1946 American Society for Quality Control is founded.

Walter Reuther becomes president of United Auto Workers' (UAW) Union.

Peter Drucker publishes *The Concept of the Corporation*.

1947 Norbert Wiener publishes *Cybernetics*.

1948 H. B. Maynard introduces the concept of "Methods Time Measurement."

Larry D. Miles develops "Value Analysis" at General Electric.

Shigeo Shingo develops "Process-based Machine Layout."

Institute of Industrial Engineers (IIE) is founded.

Soichiro Honda founds Honda Motor Company.

1949 Ralph M. Barnes publishes *Motion and Time Study*.

North Atlantic Treaty is signed.

1950 Marvin E. Mundel publishes *Motion and Time Study, Improving Productivity*.

Shigeo Shingo develops the "Single-minute Exchange of Dies" (SMED).

Kaoru Ishikawa develops the cause-and-effect diagram with the addition of cards (CEDAC).

1951 W. Edwards Deming and Joseph M. Juran begin training the Japanese on quality control.

Deming Prize is established.

Joseph M. Juran publishes *The Quality Control Handbook*, which is translated into Japanese.

1952 Industrial engineering role and sampling study conducted at American Society of Mechanical Engineers (ASME).

1954 American Motors forms from Hudson & Nash companies.

Abraham Maslow publishes *Motivation and Personality.*

1955 95% of cars in the US are domestically built.

Shigeo Shingo begins Toyota Motor Group lectures on "Separation of Workers and Machines."

Videotape is invented.

1956 New definition of industrial engineering is offered by the Institute of Industrial Engineers (IIE).

1957 Shigeo Shingo introduces the "Scientific Thinking Mechanism" for production improvements.

Chris Argyris publishes *Personality and Organizations.*

R. L. Morrow publishes *Motion and Time Study.*

1958 Herbert A. Simon publishes *Organizations.*

Nikita Khrushchev becomes Premier of the Soviet Union.

1959 Fidel Castro becomes Prime Minister of Cuba.

1960 Douglas M. McGregor publishes *The Human Side of Enterprise.*

Nissan wins the Deming Quality Prize.

1961 Lawrence D. Miles publishes *Techniques of Value Analysis and Engineering.*

Rensis Lickert publishes *New Patterns of Management.*

Shigeo Shingo devises the concepts of "Zero Quality Control," "Source Inspection," and the "Poka-yoke System."

1962 Quality circles begin at Toyota.

Masaaki Imai establishes the Kaizen Institute.

1963 H. B. Maynard publishes the *Industrial Engineering Handbook*.

Gerald Nadler publishes *Work Design*.

1965 Environmental Protection Agency passes the Clean Air Act restricting emissions.

Toyota wins the Deming Prize for Quality.

1966 Frederick Hertzberg publishes *Work and the Nature of Man*.

1968 F. J. Roethlisberger publishes "Man in Organization" essays.

US Department of Defense publishes *Principles and Application of Value Engineering*.

1969 Shigeo Shingo develops "Pre-automation" and "Single-minute Exchange of Dies."

1970 Clean Air Act calls for 90% reduction in pollution.

American Society of Tool and Manufacturing Engineers (ASTME) becomes the Society of Manufacturing Engineers (SME).

1971 Taiichi Ohno completes the Toyota Production System.

1972 Federal Water Pollution Control Act restricts pollution in lakes and rivers.

1973 Oil embargo causes panic—and drastic measures are taken—causing Japan to become leaner and more efficient.

First systems engineering conference at the American Institute of Industrial Engineers (AIIE) is held.

1974 Ford sees Mazda improving with kaizen.

1975 Shigeo Shingo extols the "Non-stock Production System."

1976 R. Muramatsu and H. Miyazaka publish "A New Approach to Production Systems Through Developing Human Factors in Japan."

1978 Ikuro Takano publishes "Complete Information of the Toyota Production System."

1979 Ford buys 25% of Mazda to learn the Japanese manufacturing system first-hand.

1980 Matsushita Electric uses Mikuni Method.

Shigeo Shingo publishes *Study of the Toyota Production System from an Industrial Engineering Viewpoint*.

1981 Shigeo Shingo's *Study of the Toyota Production System from an Industrial Engineering Viewpoint* is published in English.

1982 F. Aona publishes "Toyota's Strategy."

1985 Shigeo Shingo publishes *A Revolution in Manufacturing—The SMED System*.

1986 Shigeo Shingo publishes *Zero Quality Control: Source Inspection and the Poka-Yoke System*.

Marvin E. Mundel publishes *Motion and Time Study: Improving Productivity*.

First personal computer virus, Brain, starts to spread.

Space shuttle Challenger disintegrates 73 seconds after launch, killing its crew of six astronauts.

1987 Channel Tunnel construction is initiated on December 1.

1988 Volkswagen closes its Westmorland County, Pennsylvania plant after 10 years of operation. It was the first plant built by a non-American automaker in the US.

Shigeo Shingo publishes *Nonstock Production: The Shingo System for Continuous Improvement*.

1989 Shigeo Shingo publishes *A Study of the Toyota Production System from an Industrial Engineering Viewpoint*.

Tiananmen Square protests of 1989 take place, also known as the Tiananmen Square Massacre (June 4).

1990 First McDonald's fast-food restaurant in Moscow, USSR opens on January 31.

1991 Soviet Union is dissolved as Gorbachev resigns; Communism fails as a form of government.

1992 President Bush and Soviet leader Yeltsin proclaim the end of the "Cold War."

1993 Mosaic is developed by Marc Andreeson. It becomes the dominant navigating system for the World Wide Web.

1994 Initial commerce sites are established and mass-marketing campaigns are launched via e-mail, introducing the term "spamming" to the Internet vocabulary.

1995 Russian space station, Mir, greets first Americans as the US shuttle docks.

1996 Approximately 45 million people are using the Internet, with roughly 30 million of those in the US and Canada.

1997 Tune-up and repair work on the Hubble Space Telescope is started by astronauts from the space shuttle Discovery.

The comet Hale-Bopp has its closest approach to Earth.

1998 Ford Motor Company announces buyout of Volvo car operations for $6.45 billion.

Google is founded.

1999 Euro currency is introduced.

The Roth 401k is introduced by Senator William V. Roth.

Honda's Insight™ is the first hybrid fuel automobile imported into the US.

2000 Y2K passes without the serious, widespread computer failures and malfunctions that were predicted.

Montgomery Ward goes out of business after 128 years in the retail business.

2001 Nearly 3,000 people are killed in September 11th terrorist attacks on the World Trade Center in New York City, the Pentagon in Arlington, Virginia, and rural Shanksville, Pennsylvania.

2002 The ex-currencies of all Euro members officially cease to be legal tender.

The Last Toyota Supra™ is made at the Tahara plant in Japan.

2003 Space shuttle Columbia disintegrates over Texas upon re-entry, killing seven astronauts aboard.

2004 Space Ship One becomes the first privately funded space plane to achieve space flight.

2005 Ireland completes metrication.

Kyoto Protocol comes into effect, without the support of the US and Australia.

2006 Society of Manufacturing Engineers (SME) offers lean certifications (three levels, bronze, silver, and gold) developed in collaboration with the Association for Manufacturing Excellence (AME), and the Shingo Prize.

Appendix B

Glossary of Lean Terms

A

abnormality management—The ability to immediately detect an irregularity that is in violation of *standard operation* and control it.

activity-based costing—An accounting system that tracks costs to a product based on the amount of resources used.

affinity diagram—A brainstorming tool where everyone in a group writes down their ideas. Then the ideas are grouped and realigned by subject matter in a chart and discussed.

agile manufacturing—An approach using techniques that add to the flexibility of a process, thus reducing the impact of product mixes and volume changes.

andon—A Japanese term for a *visual control* device that constantly shows the current status of production and equipment, alerting team members to emerging problems or shortages. For example, in an assembly plant, the means by which workers can stop the track to signal a problem—often by pulling a rope—an andon cord.

arrow diagram—Visual directive symbols used within Pert charts to show the steps necessary to complete a plan.

ASME—American Society of Mechanical Engineers.

autonomation—Equipment automated to be able to detect the production of a single defective part.

B

backflush—A computer-based technique of not subtracting parts from *inventory* control until all assemblies are completed.

baka-yoke—A foolproof system that is usually part of *autonomation* (Japanese)—same as *poka-yoke*.

balanced plant—A factory where capacity is perfectly equitable with market demand.

balanced scorecard—A measure that balances the strategic intent of the current plan and gives weight to more important measures.

baseline—A statistic that compares new metric results with previous metrics, which are deemed to be "standards." Comparison is made to determine the effects of improvements.

batch and queue—Refers to the traditional *mass-production* environment wherein large lots of parts are made and then sent in batches to the next operation.

benchmark—A performance measure where best known processes and practices in current use in industry are compared to one another and to those in use at the investigating organization.

bottleneck—A choke point in a process resulting from line imbalances, which limits the throughput of the entire manufacturing process.

brownfield—An established manufacturing environment with *batch and queue* manufacturing processes and set minds.

business process reengineering—Restructuring or redesigning operational processes so they better reflect the core competency of the business and address customer-oriented concerns.

business renewal—Within a company, the strategically initiated process of periodically re-evaluating all core competencies and adjusting actions as needed.

C

CAD—Computer-aided design, more specifically, drawing by computer generation and not by hand.

CAM—Computer-aided manufacturing—all those automated, computerized functions that aid the manufacture of products, including computer-aided design (*CAD*) and other computer-driven programs, such as computer numerical control (*CNC*).

catchball—see *hoshin kanri* (Japanese term).

cause-and-effect diagram— An illustration used to analyze the characteristics of a process or situation. Also known as a fishbone graph or cause-and-effect diagram with the addition of cards (CEDAC).

cell—Machines arranged in a closed-loop system to manufacture a family of parts, typically in a U-shaped layout, which minimizes the space required and enables an operator to run *single-piece flow*.

cellular manufacturing— Alignment of production machines in proper sequence so operator(s) remain within the cell to continually load and unload machines in sequence, without leaving to get materials.

chaku-chaku—A method of *single-piece flow* in which an operator takes a part from machine to machine, to load. (The Japanese term means load-load.)

champion—An individual, at any level in an organization, who is assigned to lead the implementation and integration of *lean*.

change agent—The main driver whose mission is to convert from *batch-and-queue* processes to the future ideal state, which is *lean manufacturing*.

changeover—All actions required to switch from producing one part configuration to another, including the replacement of tools, dies, or fixtures on machines.

check sheet—A hardcopy form designed to tabulate the results of a situation.

CNC—Computer numerical control, is a type of automation that directs machines as they produce parts via a program running on a binary computer system.

co-makership—Also known as strategic partnering, an initiative that focuses on joining with suppliers of goods or services to include them in the process of defining and delivering value to the organization.

concurrent engineering— Refers to product design, development, production planning, and procurement processes taking place as far as possible in advance, in parallel rather than in series, and using multidisciplinary, project-oriented, team-based organizational structures supported by electronic information management and communication systems. The collaborative input of all concerned parties, including manufacturing, sales, and customers, is shared from a project's conception, enabling problem solving early on.

constraint—An operational *bottleneck*, which limits the output rate of a process and thus the entire system. Also known as the slowest task in a process.

continuous improvement—The definition of *kaizen*—it is the philosophy of making frequent, ongoing changes to production processes, the cumulative results of which lead to high levels of quality and efficiency, decreasing variation, decreasing costs, and improving the effectiveness of an organization. It requires a commitment to cultural change, which empowers workers to constantly make positive changes.

control chart—A hardcopy diagram used to track the two types of variation: the inevitable and abnormal.

CQM—Company-wide quality management, it is an offshoot of total quality management (*TQM*).

cross-functional management—Typically used with hoshin planning, it is the utilization of the combined expertise of individuals who represent several functional constituencies within an organization.

cross-functional team—A group comprised of representatives from several functional disciplines in an enterprise.

cycle time—The time required to complete one sequence of an operation, at one workstation, by one operator.

D

demand flow—A *pull system* or system that produces an exact order quantity required by the customer, and not to a predetermined schedule.

diagnosis—The structured, strategic, and tactical process of identifying opportunities for improvement in an enterprise.

E

early equipment management—Focusing on *total productive maintenance*, a strategy encompassing all activities directed at optimizing *overall equipment effectiveness*.

EDP—Electronic data processing, which refers to using a computer to compute difficult mathematical equations.

elemental time—Time allotted to a specific operational step within standard work.

employee involvement—Participation in decision making by employees at all levels to further the implementation of lean initiatives within an organization.

empowerment—The leadership act of transferring decision making and implementation to employees at all levels of an organization.

external setup—The work elements of tooling setup that can be performed while the machine is still running production.

F

factory within a factory—A complete product-based, flow manufacturing facility resulting from the success of *lean* initiatives, also known as a *focused factory*.

FEI—Focused equipment improvement—a specialized application of *total productive maintenance* wherein there is a concentrated effort to improve equipment performance.

FIFO—First-in-first-out—a method used in accounting for *inventory* cost, meaning the first (older) product on the shelf is the first used. It is typically used in the bakery or perishable foods industry.

FILO—First-in-last-out—a method used in accounting for *inventory* cost, meaning the first (older) product on the shelf is the last used.

FINO—First-in-never-out—a phrase indicating the first product on the shelf is never used. This is what sometimes happens to material in *batch-and-queue* operations.

five S—Five Japanese words beginning in the letter "s" that relate to levels of cleanliness. They are seiri, seiton, seiso, seiton, and shitsuke. Translated into English they are sort, set in order, shine, standardize, and sustain. They prescribe the method for obtaining an orderly and clean environment.

five whys—Taiichi Ohno's practice of asking "why" five times to get to the root cause of a problem.

flow—The movement of a part through a manufacturing process continuously until its completion.

FMS—Flexible manufacturing system—a system comprised of computer numerically controlled machines linked together and driven by computer-generated programs. The machines are capable of making many varieties of parts through this automation.

focused factory—Contrary to a batch-and-process-based operation, it is the result of implementing *cells* in a product-based manufacturing system within a *lean* manufacturing environment.

FPQ—First pass quality rate—a lean metric representing a manufacturing operation's first-pass success rate, expressed as a percentage.

G

gap analysis—A comparison of existing manufacturing results to projected results once improvements are implemented.

global production system—The *Toyota Production System* as it is applied world-wide.

graph—A visual tool that shows comparisons of data in a variety of ways—using circles (pie), columns, lines, dots, and a multitude of other illustrations and symbols.

greenfield—A new design for a new production facility that incorporates *lean* thinking and tools from the beginning.

group technology (GT)—A manufacturing philosophy based on the identification and exploitation of the underlying similarity of part shapes and manufacturing processes. By grouping similar parts into part families, it is possible to reduce costs through more effective design rationalization and design data retrieval, lower stock levels and purchase quantities, simplify and improve production planning and control, reduce tooling costs and setup times, create *flow*-line production by machine groups/*cells*, reduce in-process *inventory*, reduce total *throughput time*, reduce NC programming costs, and more efficiently use NC machines.

H

hanedashi—The Japanese term for a device that allows a machine to automatically unload a part without the need for an operator.

heijunka—The Japanese term for the creation of a "level schedule" by sequencing orders in a repetitive pattern.

Herbie—Goldratt's coined name for a *constraint* in the production process.

histogram—A bar graph of a frequency distribution in which the widths of the bars are proportional to the classes into which the variable has been divided and the heights of the bars are proportional to the class frequencies. The variation of quality characteristics is referred to the "distribution."

honcho—Japanese word for leader or *sensei*.

hoshin kanri—The Japanese phrase referring to a strategic planning tool that focuses resources on critical initiatives to accomplish goals. Using visual matrix diagrams, three to five key objectives are selected while all others are clearly deselected. The selected objectives are translated into specific projects and deployed down to the implementation level in the firm. Progress toward key objectives is then measured on a regular basis against clear targets. "Hoshin" translates literally as "shining metal" or more poetically as "the glint from the spear of a forward guide that leads the way" and "kanri" means "control."

I

integrated flow—Same as *one-piece flow*.

internal setup—The elements of tooling *changeover* that must be performed when the machine is not running.

inventory—All raw materials, purchased parts, work in process (*WIP*), and finished goods not yet sold.

Ishikawa diagram—A problem-solving tool developed by Kaoru Ishikawa that uses a graphic description of the various process elements to analyze potential sources of variation or problems.

J

jidoka—A Japanese word that means *autonomation* with a human touch.

junjo-biki—The Japanese term for a sequenced withdrawal system or *kanban*.

just-in-time—A system for producing and delivering the right items to the right location, in correct amounts, at the right time with the elimination of *waste* as its ultimate objective.

K

kaikaku—The Japanese term for a radical change to an activity to make it *lean*.

kaizen—The Japanese term for the process of *continuous improvement*.

kaizen breakthrough—A time-based, rapid deployment methodology that employs a focused, cultural-driven, team-based approach to *continuous improvement*.

kaizen costing—Reducing manufacturing costs in existing processes and operations to be competitive with others.

kaizen teian—The Japanese phrase for suggestions or a suggestion system used in support of continuous improvement.

kanban—The Japanese term for *visual control* of the movement of materials and *inventory* throughout the plant. A "kanban" is a card containing information that follows a product through each stage along its path to completion. These cards are used to control work-in-process (*WIP*), production, and inventory flow. A kanban system consists of a set of these cards, with one being allocated for each part being manufactured. Taiichi Ohno developed the kanban system.

keiretsu—Partnering Japanese companies that band together for business advantages and strength.

L

lead time—The time it takes for one part to travel through the manufacturing process to its completion.

lean—A way of thinking and applying a group of specific tools within an organization to emulate the *Toyota Production System*, wherein the ratio of *value-added* to *non-value-added* processes is substantially greater.

lean enterprise—An organization that has adopted the *lean* philosophy and is totally focused on the continuous elimination of *non-value-added* activities and *waste*.

lean manufacturing—Streamlining processes and using fewer resources to produce more product with teams, while concentrating on *continuous improvement* of the quality, cost, and delivery aspects of the business.

lean production—Production systems characterized by optimum automation using *material requirements planning*, *just-in-time* production scheduling and *just-in-time* supplier delivery disciplines. Other features of the philosophy are quick tool *changeover* times, minimum parts and work-in-process (*WIP*) *inventory*, high levels of quality, and *continuous improvement*.

level loading—The result of *heijunka*, a production schedule that is smooth and without major fluctuations.

level selling—A system that attempts to sell at an even pace without major demand peaks.

M

machine automatic time—The pure *machine cycle time* to make one piece, exclusive of loading and unloading.

machine cycle time—*Machine automatic time* plus load and unload times.

manufacturing execution system (MES)—A system using network computing to automate production control and process automation by downloading recipes and work schedules and by uploading production results, thereby bridging the gap between business and plant floor or process control systems.

manufacturing resource planning (MRP II)—A computerized method for planning the use of a company's resources, such as scheduling raw materials, vendors, production equipment and processes. Such a system includes financial, manufacturing, and distribution management.

mass customization—A system of production that stresses the production of small lots of customized goods rather than large volumes of standardized products.

mass production—The opposite of *lean production*, large-scale manufacturing with high-volume production and output, implying pre-computer-era methods, with departmentalized operation and reliance on economies of scale to achieve low per-unit costs.

materials requirements planning (MRP)—A software module using the bill of material, *inventory* data, and the master production schedule (MPS) to calculate requirements for materials and make recommendations to release replenishment orders for materials.

matrix data analysis diagram—A more detailed graph than the *matrix diagram* (second level), it is used to show the complex interrelationships between two differing factors.

matrix diagram—A graph used to show the relationship between two differing factors.

meister—The German word for "master" or leader, and the same as a Japanese *sensei*.

milk route—The continuous path material handlers take when delivering material.

mittlestand—A German word meaning family business.

mizusumashi—The Japanese word for a person who performs *kanban* replenishment by bringing material to the line in set amounts via a set route. This person is also called a water beetle or whirligig (translations from Japanese).

monument—Any large process or machine that cannot be easily moved to facilitate *flow*-based production.

MPD—Maintenance preventive design—where maximum efficiency of machines and processes is designed-in to begin with—a more advanced *Toyota Production System* trait.

muda—The Japanese term for *waste*, of which there are 10 forms.

multi-machine operation—A production layout incorporating multiple machines, wherein operators are required to run more than one machine continuously.

mura—A Japanese term for the variation of process quality, product cost, and delivery.

muri—A Japanese term meaning unreasonableness; in manufacturing, customer demand exceeds capacity.

N

nagara system—A Japanese scheme for accomplishing two or more activities with one motion.

non-value added—Any activity that adds cost or time without adding value to the process.

O

OEE—Overall equipment effectiveness—the primary metric of total preventive maintenance (***TPM***), for which the equation is: machine or equipment availability rate × machine or equipment performance rate × quality rate.

Ohno, Taiichi—Person referred to as the inventor of the ***Toyota Production System.***

one-piece flow—A system where product moves through manufacture without stopping, one-by-one. For example, work is done in cells, a piece at a time as opposed to a ***batch-and-queue*** process.

one-piece production—***Just-in-time*** flow manufacture of single parts.

one-touch exchange of dies—A tooling ***changeover*** with one component or "touch" to change.

one-touch setup—The method used to facilitate quick change of tooling, fixtures, and dies, which employs snap-together connections as opposed to screws.

open-book management—A process where all facets of a company's financial information is made available.

operation—An activity performed on a product by a single machine or process.

operator cycle time—Time needed for an operator to complete a sequence of operations, minus waiting time.

order cycle—Also known as the ***kanban*** cycle, the time interval between production orders, which is usually measured in days.

P

pacemaker—The technique of pacing a process to ***takt*** time.

pareto diagram—A bar graph used to visualize the priority of data sets.

PDPC—Process decision program chart—a special chart used in operations research.

point kaizen—An improvement activity directed specifically at one workstation or *bottleneck* and performed with a minimum team in two or three days.

poka-yoke—The Japanese term for mistake-proofing processes, also known as *baka-yoke*.

policy deployment—Also known as *hoshin kanri*, a strategic planning tool that focuses resources on critical initiatives to achieve goals.

predictive maintenance—Advanced total productive maintenance (*TPM*), where the frequency of maintenance is based on the historical records of equipment performance prior to failure.

pre-production planning—a systematic method of analyzing potential new products to determine their feasibility, cost, and components when manufactured in a *lean* environment.

process—A series of individual operations required to complete a product.

process capacity table—A chart used in the machining environment, which compares machine loading to available capacity.

process map—A workflow diagram that uses the x-axis to indicate process time and the y-axis to indicate participants and tasks.

product family—A group of related products with compatible attributes that can be run in the same *cell*.

product quantity analysis—Used in the course of conducting *kaizen* events to see the relationship between products and the quantity of products to determine flows. It groups parts into families for process comparison purposes.

production smoothing—Also known as *heijunka*, the creation of a level schedule by sequencing orders in a repetitive pattern, which over time eliminates customer demand fluctuation by producing every part every day.

pull system—A system of production driven from the last operation, which draws from the previous operation exactly what is needed to satisfy the customer at the end.

Q

QS-9000—A quality standard based on ISO 9000 and used by the American domestic automobile manufacturers to register their suppliers.

quality audit—A systematic and independent examination to determine if quality related activities are implemented effectively and comply with quality systems and/or quality standards.

quality circle—Originating in 1962, a cross-departmental group of plant workers who meet to discuss ways to improve quality.

quality function deployment (QFD)—A structured method employing matrix analysis for linking what the market requires to how it will be accomplished in the development effort. This method is most valuable during product development when a multifunctional team agrees on how customer needs relate to product specifications and features.

queue time—The period of time a product spends waiting to be processed or moved.

R

re-engineering—The redefinition of a company's internal processes.

relation diagram—Also known as a ***cause-and-effect diagram***, an illustration used to analyze the characteristics of a process or situation.

right-sizing—The process of eliminating ***monuments*** by replacing them with in-line, appropriately sized equipment.

S

scatter diagram—A graph in which two pieces of corresponding data are plotted using dots to show their relationship.

sensei—Japanese word for teacher or master (same as the German word ***meister***).

Shingo, Shigeo—Considered the master consultant to industry and dean of productivity and quality, he is the author of more than 20 books.

shusa—Japanese term for a powerful and strong person, usually a team leader.

single-piece flow—A line where parts are processed one at a time and moved one at a time through to completion.

six sigma—Also called total quality management (*TQM*), it is a vision of quality, which equates with only 3.4 defects per million opportunities for each product or service transaction. The methodology relies heavily on statistical techniques to measure success.

SMED—Single-minute exchange of die—refers to all forms of tooling, including dies, which can be changed over in single-digit minutes (or less) from the last good finished part using the existing tooling, to the next good part using the new.

spaghetti diagram—A path on a plant layout that shows the actual distance and sequence taken during manufacture. The graph looks like a plate of spaghetti when drawn.

standard costing—A management accounting method, which allocates costs (or earned hours) to products based on the number of machine hours and labor hours available. It is also the method used to estimate production capacities.

standard operation—The best combination of people and machines utilizing the least amount of labor, space, *inventory*, and equipment.

standard work combination sheet—A document showing the sequence of production steps to be performed by the operator, including the time-consuming activities of each process, such as machine run times.

standard work in process—The minimal quantity of material required to complete one cycle of work without delay.

standard work instruction—The written description of exactly how a part is to be made by workers, specifying *takt* time, *cycle time*, sequence of operations, etc.

standard work layout—A diagram of a workstation or *cell* showing the sequence of standard work.

statistical quality control (SQC)—A procedure that applies the laws of probability and statistical techniques to the observed characteristics of a product or process.

stop-the-line authority—When problems occur, the operator is empowered to stop the process to prevent bad parts from being produced.

sub-optimization (of equipment)—Keeping all equipment running without consequence, which usually wastes material.

supermarket—On the shop floor, the line-side location for parts to be run in a *cell*.

supply chain management—The use of information technology to endow automated intelligence to an ever-growing network of vendors and raw material suppliers.

T

takt—The German term for the pace at which the customer requires a part. Takt time is equal to the customer demand divided by time available, minus any planned subtractions of time for breaks, etc.

target cost—The projected expense of making an item, which can not be exceeded.

team—A group of persons who participate in or manage a project.

team leader—The person who captains a team. He or she is responsible for ensuring that milestones and deliverables are achieved.

therblig—A term coined by Frank B. Gilbreth (Gilbreth spelled backwards) referring to the 18 elemental human movements in time-motion study.

throughput time—The period of time it takes to complete one part through the manufacturing process, including all *queue times* and non-value-added activities.

time-based strategy—Business objectives built around economy-of-time principles.

Toyota Production System—A philosophy and methodology for the elimination of *waste*, which uses 14 principles based upon 40 years of internal improvements at Toyota.

TPM—Total productive maintenance, which comprises a formal plan for preventive maintenance to ensure that machines and equipment are always able to perform their required tasks without fail and at the designed rates. In theory, never experiencing lost production time because of unscheduled maintenance. Machine operators are responsible for daily cleaning and minor adjustment of the machines they work on.

TQM—total quality management—a comprehensive and structured approach to organizational management that seeks to improve the quality of products and services through ongoing refinements in response to continuous feedback from customers.

tree diagram—A chart that shows the interrelationship of goals and measures. In value engineering, it is used in functional analysis.

V

value added—The act or process by which tangible product features or intangible service attributes are bundled, combined, or packaged with other features and attributes in response to customer feedback. An activity that adds value to the customer, and for which the customer is willing to pay.

value analysis—Assessing the activities involved in producing a product to determine the percentage of actual *value-added* activities.

value stream—All activities in the manufacturing process required to complete a product or part family—from the initial order to the hands of the customer.

value stream mapping—A pictorial depiction of the complete manufacturing process showing *value-added* and *non-value-added* steps with specific identifying details.

visual control—The use of standards in the workplace, which make it obvious if anything is out of order. For example, the arrangement and labelling of all necessary tools and devices in plain view and closest to where they are used. Such order is intended to actually control or guide the action of workers.

visual factory—Refers to *visual controls* and displays used to relate information and data to employees in the work area.

voice of the customer (VOC)—A process for eliciting needs from consumers via structured, in-depth interviews. Needs are obtained through indirect questioning to gain an understanding of how consumers meet their needs, and more importantly, why they choose a particular solution.

W

waste—same as *muda*. Any activity that utilizes equipment, materials, parts, space, employee time, or other corporate resources beyond the minimum amount required for *value-added* operations and to ensure manufacturability.

WIP—Work in process; the *inventory* waiting between operations.

work sequence—The orderly and exact steps an operator takes to perform his or her job.

Appendix C

Team Exercise: Deluxe Elaborate Manufacturing Company (DEMCO)

DIRECTIONS

As an exercise to reinforce kaizen knowledge and learning, the following case study of Deluxe Elaborate Manufacturing Company (DEMCO) may be read by a kaizen team in training, followed by answering the questions listed in the Team Assignment section. It takes approximately 15 minutes to read the case study.

BACKGROUND INFORMATION

DEMCO has been manufacturing hand tools since 1940. The products manufactured are electronic and/or electrically driven standard and special-purpose hand tools.

The Abernathy family started the company in their garage in Rockford, Illinois. The company soon outgrew the garage, so they bought property and moved to a building on the edge of town. The Abernathy family controlled management of DEMCO until a large aerospace company bought it 12 years ago. Since then, the company has struggled to upgrade its management style as well as recapitalize the business.

Over the years more buildings have been added to the company. Manufacturing is now done in eight buildings, all of which are connected. The main offices are in a year-old, three-story building across the street from the main factory. And there is a 200,000 ft^2 (18,581 m^2) warehouse adjacent to the new office where $3.8 million dollars in inventory is stored. In addition, there are plating facilities on the other side of town and a leased building about six blocks away where the electronics equipment and tools are assembled.

The company now has approximately 3,000 stock-keeping units (SKUs) within 10 major product families. The scrap rate is 4.8%, but rework is 12% across all operations. Parts usually require additional work other than what is outlined on the process sheets.

The work force is made up of local people; most are originally from the area. The average worker is 44 years old. About 15% of workers have less than one year of seniority. The attrition rate is 8% and the absenteeism rate is 3.8%. And, 75% of management has been with the company 20 years or more. Most operators have relatives working at DEMCO too. The company is unionized and has been for 30 years. Workers are members of Amalgamated Manufacturing Workers of America (AMWA). There is also another union that represents the tradesmen, the Association of Tradesmen (AT).

THE DILEMMA

Tools are sold through dealers and special commercial accounts.

Business at DEMCO has been steadily growing at 8–10% per year. However, the competition has been growing at an estimated 13–15% per year. Profits have been flat with no increase in the past 18 months, despite additional revenues.

Corporate management has challenged DEMCO to "shape-up" or they will "ship-out" the work to Asia. They have mandated a 5% per year improvement in profit. Two new innovative products have been purchased from another company and a decision has to be made as to where they will be produced. The question is, "Is DEMCO the right choice for this additional work based on current conditions?"

UNION INVOLVEMENT

There has never been a strike at DEMCO. However, there have been rumors that the parent company might consider moving the plant to Asia to save on labor costs. Both unions are apprehensive about the future. The president of the AMWA union is 33-year-old setup man, Lynn Townsend, who has been with DEMCO for 12 years. The president of AT is Billy Butler, an electrician with 33 years of seniority.

The unions are willing to do whatever is necessary to keep the work in Rockford. Lynn Townsend and Billy Butler have heard that lean manufacturing might be the salvation. They are curious to learn more to determine if it is something that should be tried at DEMCO.

RECRUITING THE BEST PEOPLE

Recently, DEMCO broadened its recruitment efforts. The company sought to hire more talented managers, engineers, and tradesmen—many from out of state. (Relocation costs were reimbursed by DEMCO.) As a result, several talented managers, engineers, and technicians have joined DEMCO's work force. They are experienced in areas of the business that the "home-grown" leadership lacks. Some have extensive experience in lean; others more extensive technical training.

KAIZEN ROLL-OUT

DEMCO is formulating plans to roll out a plan to hold kaizen events throughout the plant.

Paul Keefer has been plant manager for six months. Previously he was assistant manager at another division, where he was on the team charged with promoting lean throughout the corporation. The DEMCO plant was chosen to pilot a kaizen event. On Paul's staff is Warren Wilson, the controller; Gerald Bixby, a 33-year veteran and operations manager; James Dumore, manager of quality; Karen Johnson, director of human resources; William Ovitz, director of information technology; Brenda Stabil, production manager; Roger Summers, manager of maintenance; Eduardo Polaski, director of engineering; and Peter Paytol, manager of shipping and receiving. Most recently, Dinty Moore was promoted to lean champion and is responsible for lean implementation.

So far, most improvement training has been classroom oriented for management and technical employees only. And, the links between training and specific business needs have been weak. To prepare the shop-floor people for the roll out, each department is to be responsible for training. Each supervisor is free to choose the appropriate training, then to proceed with instruction. Until now, there was not an official mandate to train everyone on anything other than what had already been taught on specific subjects. The focus of previous training was in the following areas:

- statistical process control (SPC) (inspection department had only one person trained);

- just-in-time (DEMCO tried to pilot a small tool line six months ago, but the line regressed to its original state, which was attributed to no follow-up);

- quality circles (for the past three months weekly meetings were held to talk about how to reduce scrap/rework in selected production areas);

- material requirements planning (MRP) (production control had two classes);

- total quality control (TQC) (foremen took a two-day class);

- 5S (application was voluntary and at the discretion of the area foreman);

- ISO 9000 certification (Karen Johnson was trainer and auditor); and

- kanban (American Production and Inventory Control Society members are working to be certified, nothing completed).

Choosing the Area

On a monthly basis, management planned to explore all the improvement scenarios available on the shop floor. The ones that seemed the best would be the ones adopted for kaizen. Kind of like the "flavor-of-the-month" approach. However, with the threat of outsourcing looming, the areas in particular need of improvement are manufacturing lead time, which now averages 12 weeks for special tools not in the warehouse. Those tools in stock are available for immediate shipment. But back-orders make up about 45% of the total orders, and the production schedule is constantly being adjusted to accommodate filling late orders.

Paul recently met with Dinty to review the corporate plan to implement lean at DEMCO. Paul explained to Dinty that by holding "kaizen blitzes" in each area, the whole plant could be re-laid out into cells, thus reducing the floor space needed, reducing labor content on each product, increasing profits, and greatly reducing manufacturing lead time. Not to mention that plant-wide quality would dramatically improve, and morale and safety would improve too. Typical kaizen event projects are outlined in Table C-1.

Forming the Team

Since the first meeting of Paul and Dinty, Dinty has been focusing his time and attention on learning all about lean. He attended a public kaizen event at a supplier's facility where he was a team member. This was his first exposure to kaizen. Two weeks later he again participated in another event, this time as a co-leader. Since then, Dinty has read available literature and spoken to many people at companies who have held events to find out what it would take to hold an event at DEMCO. Dinty has assembled a staff of six core team members who will help him implement lean throughout the plant.

The First Kaizen Event

Last week Dinty and the core team held DEMCO's first kaizen event. However, the results were not as good as he expected. The event was completely planned and executed by the core team, but was met with only limited success.

There were some comments made that Gerald Bixby conducted the event in the same manner he

Table C-1. Typical Kaizen Event Projects

- Replace long conveyor assembly lines with cells.
- Combine operations, change, or improve a process.
- Reduce setup times using single-minute exchange of dies (SMED).
- Reduce lot sizes; reduce work in process.
- Hold a visual factory or 5S exercise only.
- Implement a new product or establish new metrics.
- Establish a milk route or supermarket—water spider.
- Level the load schedule.
- Establish maintenance programs or improve overall equipment effectiveness (OEE) on one machine.
- Increase or decrease production based on new takt time.
- Change from an automated process to a manual process.
- Move from one plant to another.
- Make safety improvements.
- Train for future kaizen events.

runs the shop, with an iron fist and a loud mouth. Gerald stayed in his office most of the time except to make his nightly tour of the production areas. The team thought this was good because whenever he appeared, he would only complain about something. Some of the comments from the team members indicated that they felt intimidated. The team leaders were reluctant to be innovative because Gerald had said in the past that certain ideas were no good and would not work. In his own words, "I tried them all before and I know what worked and what didn't, so don't waste my time!" In addition, he did not appear to be properly prepared for the event. When addressing the team, on occasion he wandered into subjects that were irrelevant; his stories of how he conquered the war against the union came up frequently. One union member complained to Billy Butler but nothing was done to stop Gerald from telling his stories.

It was difficult for the teams to do time studies because there were not enough operators to run the lines. They had to stop and move over to the next station then start again. When it was time to try the new layout and move the machines, Gerald would not release the line so the changes could be made. One team had to settle for simulating production to prove out their improvements because no production was scheduled for three days and the team was not informed of this prior to starting the event.

Two team leaders complained of having too many people on their teams. And, the area supervisors were reluctant to challenge the teams' recommendations or implement them. Gerald would have to make those decisions, as he had done before.

The operators were wondering why all the changes were happening. Nobody bothered to inform them in advance about the event and what affect it would have on them. They were uncomfortable with outsiders coming into their area and changing things, especially without including them.

An operator mentioned that one line being kaizened was scheduled to be phased out in six months. Another mentioned that no one indicated what would happen to the operator who was freed-up as a result of improvements.

Dinty was very busy during the event. There was no demand data available for the teams and several team members were called away quite frequently on "other" business. Once Dinty had to run to the hardware store and get cleaning supplies, because those for the event were mistakenly used by the night shift janitor and locked up because he did not want to lose them.

In spite of the difficulties, there were some good results from the event. However, it still fell short of expectations. Dinty met with the core team immediately after the event to evaluate the past week. Unfortunately, the event was not attended by Paul or any of his staff (monthly budget meeting). But Billy Butler and Lynn Townsend did attend. Gerald had his secretary read the overheads to save time and limit team comments.

Gerald did not think it was a good idea to have any kind of celebration. What would the other operators think about being left out? Instead, the team members had their pictures taken with Gerald as a group (not in teams).

THE KAIZEN TEAM'S MISSION

Dinty must continue holding kaizen events if DEMCO is to increase profit by 5% per year. He has asked you and your team to help him conduct a series of events. The ex-

pected outcome is to meet the corporate goals of reducing throughput time by 50%, reducing labor by 20%, improving quality so rework can be eliminated, and freeing up space so the new products can be made at DEMCO instead of outsourced elsewhere.

Paul has told Dinty that he can have anyone he chooses on the event teams. And he can choose what he thinks are the areas that will get the best results quickly, as long as he can justify to Paul his choices. It is okay to spend money. After proving that kaizen events work, Paul can get more money added to the budget.

TEAM ASSIGNMENT

You and your team are to:

1. Identify the key lessons learned from the first kaizen event. (20 minutes)

2. Identify what you would do differently. Be specific. (20 minutes)

3. Identify the areas of focus for the next four events using Tables C-2 and C-3. (20 minutes)

4. Identify the team members for each event by reviewing

Table C-2. DEMCO's 10 Major Product Lines

Number	Product Line	Business Volume	Revenue	Scrap Rate	Work in process/ Inventory	Back-order	Manufacturing Lead Time
1	Small hand tools	22%	9%	6%	$356,000	$267,000	34 days
2	Medium hand tools	13%	11%	5%	$187,000	$237,000	29 days
3	Large hand tools	4%	2%	4%	$235,000	$199,800	41 days
4	Electric-powered hand tools	12%	13%	6.5%	$287,800	$202,000	40 days
5	Electric-powered special tools	3%	3%	7%	$167,900	$ 34,500	28 days
6	Electronic specialty tools	10%	18%	2%	$ 34,600	$ 16,800	62 days
7	Original equipment manufacturer tools	12%	5%	2.3%	$238,900	$302,900	44 days
8	Export and licensee tooling	5%	7%	1%	$239,900	$190,000	48 days
9	Low-volume special equipment	2%	3%	0.3%	$ 66,300	$ 43,200	70 days
10	Replacement parts	17%	24%	4.6%	$1,700,000	$553,000	22 days

the resumes of individuals in the next section. (20 minutes)

5. Explain your selection logic for numbers 3 and 4.

6. What methodology did you use to make the selections?

7. Select a facilitator to lead a 10-minute report out of numbers 1–6. It is all right to make assumptions. Just be sure to note them and explain in the report out. Use visuals to help clarify your selection process.

If this case study is being read by many teams in a group training setting, each team may question the others regarding their selections and criteria used. Each team should be prepared to rationalize and justify its selections.

Choosing Team Members for the Four Events

Following are the resumes of individuals available to serve on the teams. Choose from them to complete number four in the preceding section.

Table C-3. Facilities Required to Manufacture Parts (numbers refer to products listed in Table C-2)

Facility	Product Number
Stamping/forging	1,2,3,4,5,6,7,9,10
Assembly area one	1,2,3, 4,5,7
Assembly area two	4,5,6
Assembly area three	9
Final assembly	1,2,3,4
Heavy machining	1,2,3,4,5,6,7,8,9,10
Heat treating	1,2,3,4,5,7,8,9,10
Plating	1,2,3,4,5,7,8,9,10
Grinding	1,2,3,4,5,7,8,9,10
Electronic assembly (Park Drive)	6
Packing and shipping	1,2,3,4,5,6,7,8,9,10
Painting	3,4,5,6,7,8,9
Welding	1,2,3,4,5,7,8,9,10

Exempt Employee Roster

Plant manager, Paul Keefer— Age 42, he has been with the parent company six years. He has been plant manager for six months and previously was assistant manager at another division. He was on the core team charged with promoting lean throughout the corporation. Paul has been actively involved in lean for about four years. He has formal training as an engineer and 18 years total manufacturing experience, 12 years as an engineer and six in management.

Controller, Warren Wilson— Age 44, he has 23 years with DEMCO. Promoted by corporate from the chief accountant's position, he has served the last four years as controller. Warren studied activity-based costing and computers at night school. He believes that a lean organization must change the metrics currently in use to promote change. Warren asked Dinty to consider him for the core team.

Operations manager, Gerald Bixby— Age 53, he has 33 years with the company. Gerald started out as a production operator, advanced to setup, then to supervision. He is considered to possess the most knowledge in the company about its machines and processes. Gerald participated in the first kaizen event and was very impressed. He is currently on the core team. Gerald has additional training in management by objectives (MBO), manufacturing resource planning (MRP), and quality assurance systems (QAS). He also owns a working farm of 44 acres that has been in his family for generations. All of Gerald's closest relatives are pig farmers.

Manager of quality, James Dumore— Age 29, he has an MBA from Massachusetts Institute of Technology. James was recently hired to bring new thinking to DEMCO. He has worked at the Rockford facility for 13 months. James worked in a water treatment plant in Chicago prior to that. He took many courses on statistical process control (SPC) and statistics while in school. His MBA thesis was entitled, "Probability of Life in Outer Space."

Director of human resources, Karen Johnson— Age 33, she has been with the company seven months. Previously Karen was a trainer in the human resources department at General Motors (GM).

She had training on the Toyota Production System while employed there. Karen is currently pursuing a masters' degree in industrial psychology.

Director of information technology, William Ovitz—Age 36, he has been with DEMCO for three years. He has a degree in computer technology. William believes SAP® or BAHN® are the most important additions that can be made to DEMCO. He has succeeded in getting all of DEMCO's financials computerized. William previously worked for the Chase Manhattan Bank in New York.

Production manager, Brenda Stabil—Age 49, she has been with DEMCO for 22 years. Brenda worked as a production worker, then lead, then department manager. She has been production manager for five years and has attended all the training offered by the plant. Brenda was on the first kaizen event and doubts that it will last—"Just another flavor of the month." She has two daughters working in the plant. Brenda took computer courses in night school for two years.

Manager of maintenance, Roger Summers—Age 50, he is a journeyman electrician. Roger has been with the company 32 years and manager of maintenance the past eight years. He was union president for two terms 12 years ago. Roger is known as the "fireman" for his ability to get old junk machines up and running. He has 12 skilled workers, six helpers plus six janitors on staff. Roger was on the first kaizen team but had to leave many times to "put out fires." He is also on the core team.

Director of engineering, Eduardo Polaski—Age 36, he has been with DEMCO for 15 months. He was hired to make innovations happen. Previously Eduardo worked at General Electric as specialty engineering manager. He was responsible for implementing concurrent engineering and promoting the black-belt program in GE's engineering department. He acted as a "Black Belt" there for 16 months. Eduardo has degrees in engineering and physics. He has been on the core team from the beginning.

Manager shipping/receiving, Peter Paytol—Age 30, he has been with the company 10 years. Peter began working as a forklift driver. He was soon promoted to supervisor of material handling and then to manager two years ago. Peter was co-leader on the first kaizen team. He is attending night school to become a locksmith and start his own business.

Office manager, Allison McKenzie—Age 29, she has been with the company two years. Allison manages 14 people in the front office. Most have never been out in the shop. Two employees have husbands who are familiar with kaizen and lean manufacturing so they would like to see and be part of the next event. The two have asked Dinty Moore several times to consider them for a kaizen team, but have not yet been chosen.

Sales engineer with supplier, United National Steel (UNS), Adrian Swift—UNS has held seven kaizen events involving all of its sales engineers and 40% of production personnel. Adrian invited Dinty to UNS for one of its kaizen events. UNS was ISO 9000 certified last January.

Sales and marketing manager with paint supplier, Luster Finishes, Donald Trout—Luster Finishes supplies paint to numerous lean manufacturers. The company is QS9000 certified. Don has been to

two kaizen events at customer plants within the last six months and wants his company to have regularly scheduled kaizen events too.

Sales engineer with machine-tool builder, Best Machine Company, Harold Stassen—Harold has been to Japan and seen how they do kaizen. Best Machine Company holds regular kaizen events and has a full-time lean champion.

Chief buyer for customer, SFX Company, Reginald Oxwald—Reggie attended a public event three months ago and recommended to his boss that SFX get into lean, especially kaizen events.

Purchasing agent for customer, National Hardware Sales, Arthur Tate—National Hardware Sales is a major customer of hand tools from DEMCO. Dealing with many companies that conduct kaizen events, National Hardware Sales has sent representatives to five events in the past year.

Director of lean enterprise for customer, BWM, Inc., Peter Stashey—BWM uses special equipment built by DEMCO. The Toyota Production System is in place at all of BWM's manufacturing facilities.

Rockford Community College, program for advanced technology—There are six instructors who teach numerous classes on the lean enterprise and just-in-time related subjects. The earned degree is in advanced technology. The college also has apprenticeship programs in several skilled trades areas.

Production Supervisors

Carol Butts has 12 years at DEMCO. He supervises the stamping and forging lines. The machines are old and the department works the most overtime in the plant. Quality is poor to fair. The lines are run by five operators each. There is excessive downtime due to the production schedule constantly changing, requiring frequent changeovers. This is a definite bottleneck. Two operators have kaizen experience. Carol has heard about single-minute exchange of dies (SMED) and thinks he would like to try it in his area.

Robert Nowak has 11 years with DEMCO in its grinding area. The area has 22 machines and employs 14 operators. Some machines are scattered on the other side of plant. There is extra capacity, but not enough trained operators. Quality is fair. Machines require con-

tinual adjustments. None of the operators has kaizen experience.

Rex Norad has 14 years with the company. He supervises the heat treatment of materials for all the production lines. He is also responsible for the plating operation on the other side of town. In heat treating, there are batch processes, big monuments, and long cycle times. There are six furnace operators and three material handlers in heat treating, and four operators and six material handlers at the plating plant. There are also two metallurgists, and none of the operators has kaizen experience.

Jennifer Osgood has 16 years with DEMCO in the assembly one area. She supervises the assembly of hand tools for the wholesale market. There are two lines, each with 10 operators. Two employees have lean experience. One is a new employee going to college part-time. The other is a high-school graduate who wants to become a tool-and-die maker and whose father has been to Japan for Toyota Production System training.

Rollie Barrett has eight years with DEMCO in assembly area two. The area assembles electrically powered tools for the wholesale market.

Assembly is done on two lines. One has 18 operators, the other seven. One operator comes from General United Technologies where she was on two kaizen teams. At General United Technologies, her area was 5S'd and there was company-sponsored training on SMED for all the operators and temporary personnel.

Hayden Proffitt has 17 years with DEMCO in material handling. He supervises 12 forklift operators on two shifts. None of them has lean experience.

Arithal Boysette has 22 years with DEMCO in the final assembly area for hand tools. There is one line with 14 operators. Most have been on the line for five years or more. All operators are cross-trained and rotate assignments among themselves. They have the best record for attendance in the plant. Quality is very good.

Hector Rodriguez has nine years experience as receiving supervisor. He has been with the company 11 years. Hector has a team of six unpackers and clerks. There are four temporary persons. No one has had lean training. One person is a union steward.

Miles Standish has four years with the company in the heavy machining department. There are 21 machines in the department, of which 15 are computer numerical control (CNC) machines. The department employs 13 operators. Seven have had training on the Toyota Production System and two have worked on kaizen events at previous employers. One setup man is a journeyman tool-and-die maker. Miles is a journeyman machinist and has extensive experience with setups.

Roger Ditmer has nine years with the company in assembly area three, which assembles electrically powered tools not assembled by Rollie's group. There are nine operators and three temporary persons in the area. The work schedule is very unstable. Some days there is too much work, other days no work. Assembly three is the least efficient area in the plant. It is mainly used to expedite orders and uses airfreight to deliver parts.

Robert Cook has three years with DEMCO as tool room supervisor. He supervises 11 persons: three machinists, two toolmakers, two die makers, two machine repairmen, one apprentice, and one co-op student. One toolmaker and one die maker have seen SMED. Most workers are over 50 years of age, except for an apprentice who is 19 and a co-op student from college who is 21. Robert has worked for companies that are lean and he is familiar with the Toyota Production System. He went to a kaizen event last year.

Marshall Trayburn has seven years with DEMCO at its electronics assembly facility on Park Drive. Marshall previously worked for a California company that implemented lean. Electronics products contribute the highest margin of any DEMCO product. The assembly facility shares some operations with the main plant: shipping and receiving, maintenance, tooling and engineering, and administrative staff. New product launch has been poor, but once up and running, the operation is very good. Currently there are many stock-keeping units (SKUs) for parts run through the small, cramped plant. There are also delays in releasing orders and having material on hand. This is because Park Drive relies on the main plant for these services and it now takes too long for the main plant to respond.

Three engineers at Park Drive have had exposure to lean and kaizen.

Ronald Kromm has 19 years at DEMCO in the paint room. Ron supervises six painters and two technicians. The equipment is difficult to change over and causes assembly delays waiting for the right color. Scheduling is a bottleneck. Capacity is sufficient, but constant changes are required to expedite "hot" jobs. The paint room has had OSHA compliance problems recently and received several warnings. It is currently "on warning" for safety and environmental violations.

Billy Bob Thornton came to DEMCO 10 years ago after retiring from the Navy as a shipyard welder. He is thinking about retiring from DEMCO soon. Billy Bob has told management that he will not be volunteering for any additional training. He sees no use in it as he could leave at any time. Billy Bob supervises two welding/assembly lines, mostly automated, with nine operators and two technicians. Equipment is new but needs a lot of maintenance. The lines are constantly being hammered about poor overall equipment effectiveness (OEE), which stands at only 42%.

TEAM RESULTS

Following is the documentation of several teams' conclusions and deductions, and their presentations with comments. You and your team can compare these results with those obtained in the preceding exercise.

Team One

Team One decided to make operational improvements to the chosen areas with training being secondary in importance. Within those areas, the team tried to reduce scrap and alleviate bottlenecks.

Key Lessons Learned

In discussing the case study, Team One identified the following key lessons learned.

- Leadership was poor.

- There was no visible management support.

- There was no scope or clear objectives.

- There was a lack of sufficient forward planning.

- Team member selection was poor.

- Gerald Bixby should not have been the coordinator of the first kaizen event. He was not capable of being a change agent. He intimidated people when he walked the shop floor and stayed in his office most of the day.

- The role of the coordinator was not communicated to everyone. The concepts of everyone being equal, one person one vote, etc., were not understood.

- There was inadequate training.

- There was no empowerment.

- There was no celebration.

- Teams did not present a final report out to share learning from the experience.

What Could be Done Differently

Team One came up with the following things that could be done differently on the next event.

- Change the requirement or "feeling" that the event was meant to result in cost savings only.

- Do the proper planning to ensure there is sufficient time to complete all tasks.

- Ensure people are available to man the workstations that are part of the event.

- Improve communications so the event is not perceived as just another "flavor-of-the-month." Rather, it involves a new way of thinking and is a new business philosophy.

- Empower people; let the team make the decisions, not management.

- Follow-up and complete all unfinished action items to build confidence in management's commitment to lean.

- Offer the proper training to team leaders and the coordinator.

- Clearly communicate the goals and objectives of the event and expectations for the team members.

- Have a better cross-section of personnel on the teams.

- Allow for a celebration and the recognition of team members.

Areas for the Next Four Events

Team One has chosen the following areas for the next four events:

- Heat treating—The team will begin making improvements near the end of the line and work backwards to minimize the potential for creating bottle-necks. This area is currently perceived as the worst area in the plant.

- Stamping and forging—The plan is to reduce the scrap rate and eliminate a key bottleneck. However, this area is the most difficult area to recapitalize, since most machines are monuments and there are long lead times to procure new equipment.

- Grinding—In this area, part movement is the worst; parts travel the greatest distance. Quality will improve if all machines are in one area. There is the possibility of sharing operators or one operator may be able to operate multiple machines. The area will require the most moves to improve flow.

- Welding—This area has a lot of potential, but its leadership is not eager to change.

Assumptions

- Heat treat is the highest contributor to work in process (WIP).

- Stamping and forging is the highest contributor to scrap.

- Grinding adds WIP, has a high scrap rate, and parts have the longest distance to travel to be completed.

- Welding has the next highest scrap rate and excessive WIP. It does not use the latest processes or equipment.

- New equipment will need to be purchased for the stamping and forging shop at some point in time.

Team Member Selection and Why

Heat Treating

The heat treat team consists of nine members, including the team leader. The following individuals have been chosen.

Team leader, Harold Stassen— He has industry experience with machines and tooling, plus he has been on kaizen teams before. Harold is an outsider and will bring a fresh set of eyes to an area that may need new equipment. He will bring creditability and leadership to the event.

Co-leader, Arithal Boysette— He is a good solid employee who is capable of becoming a team leader after several events. Arithal is not local, so he will not be biased.

Rex Norad—He works in the heat treating department and knows the inner workings of the area. As a team member, he will not have the only opinion as to problems or solutions. However, Rex will have the task of implementing improvements to his area, so it is important that he co-author the changes to be made there.

Warren Wilson—Since he is controller, his understanding of the area may be influential in getting funding for new equipment.

Eduardo Polaski—As director of engineering, he will be available for technical questions. Eduardo will also help to determine the feasibility of new process and new equipment scenarios. He can take the message back to top management about the real situation in the heat treating area.

In addition, there are two heat treating operators from the first shift, one operator from third shift, and one metallurgist from the satellite facility who will join the team.

Stamping and Forging

The stamping and forging team consists of nine members, including the team leader. The following individuals have been chosen.

Team leader, Adrian Swift— Adrian has had extensive exposure to kaizen events and is familiar with steel processes. Not from DEMCO, he will be impartial and neutral. This will be the first time Adrian is a team leader, but he has been a co-leader several times.

Co-leader, Carol Butts—As production supervisor, he has wealth of technical experience in the area. He will be open to seeing the potential for improvements in his department and implementing changes.

Robert Cook—As tool room supervisor, he has valuable technical knowledge of stamping tools and die construction.

In addition, there is a machinist from the tool room on day shift who is familiar with the dies and tools used in the department. He can get special tools made if required. A union steward from the stamping area will represent the union as a partner. He is fair and objective and has an open mind about change.

And, there are two operators from the stamping area on day shift. They will have to implement the changes in the department and teach the others. An operator from the night shift is also included. He will communicate to rest of the night shift the benefits of the event and train others. Should a night shift event be held, he could be a potential leader. The new employee from assembly one area whose father is a tool-and-die maker will also join the team. He is aggressive about following in his father's footsteps. He wants to tell his father he too knows about lean.

Grinding

The grinding team consists of eight members, including the team leader. The following individuals have been chosen.

Team leader, Robert Cook— He was on the previous team for the stamping and forging event. Robert knows plant personnel and politics. He is familiar with single-minute exchange of dies (SMED) and some concepts of the Toyota Production System (TPS).

Co-leader, the union steward from the stamping and forging area— He is familiar with kaizen and will ensure that workers know the union is in favor of these events. His presence will add credibility to the cause.

Other team members are a tool-and-die maker from the tool room who knows more about the details of the process and can get new tools and parts made. A forklift operator from the shipping area will also join the team to help expedite moving machines from across the plant. A lot of moving is necessary with this event. Four operators, one from each shift, also will join.

Welding

The welding team consists of seven members, including the team leader. The following individuals have been chosen.

Team leader, a tool-and-die maker from the tool room who was on a previous team as a team member will be a good fit. Industrious and well organized, he was very helpful on the last event. He has proven he can get things done and sticks to a task until completed.

Co-leader, Hector Rodriguez —A supervisor in receiving, he is in preliminary lean training and can put what he has learned thus far to work.

Billy Bob Thornton—As supervisor of the area, he will have the responsibility of maintaining improvements.

In addition, four operators from the welding area, two from each shift, will be included on the team.

Conclusion and Critique

- The key lessons learned were good observations and correct.

- The changes that Team One will make are sound.

- The areas chosen for the next events are indicative of Team One's thinking. In these areas there is a need for major changes to be made to the core processes. Rather than doing events for the learning value, the team chose to tackle the most difficult areas in the plant.

- There is some continuity to the plan but it could be better. For example, it would probably be better to do several events in the heat treating area before moving on to the next elephant, the stamping and forging area.

- Cost could be a limiting factor in what can be accomplished during the event if success is contingent upon new machines improving the department.

- Because of the many technical elements in both the heat treating and stamping and forging areas, serious thought should be given to the goals and objectives of the events. Are they realistic?

- Beginning with the two most difficult areas in regard to machinery and monuments can result in events where most of the results end up on the follow-up sheets, with little actually getting changed during the event.

- There was not enough digging for the actual numbers that would tell the whole picture. Tables C-2 and C-3 could have been made more comprehensive with additional criteria deemed important to the decision-making process.

The exercise grade is 77%—a "C." Team One's events will have limited success and require more than normal follow-up.

Team Two

Team Two chose to make operational changes rather than make changes that would have training value. Training would be stronger in later events.

Key Lessons Learned

The following is a list of key lessons learned by Team Two.

- Poor preparation caused a scattered focus.

- Scope and details were not communicated to the shop floor.

- There was no coordination of production schedules, and there was not 100% commitment of a clear calendar.

- There was no daily event schedule.

- Managers should have acted as participants, not leaders.

- There should have been a celebration.

- There should have been a mandatory follow-up with all staff.

- There was no coordination or communication with the unions.

- There was need for a strong team leader who was not biased.

- A report-out should have taken place to document all the team members' experiences from the event.

- The core team was not correctly trained to plan the first event.

- Enthusiasm was missing.

What Could be Done Differently

Team Two came up with the following list of what could be done differently.

- Define the scope and objectives clearly.

- Schedule the event weeks in advance.

- Pick the team and start preparation work as soon as possible.

- Use the college for overview training prior to team selection.

- Conduct team member meetings to review check sheets.

- Develop a list of supplies needed and have them on-hand for the event.

- Plan the week's schedule and agenda, and publish it before the event.

- Make preliminary maintenance arrangements.

- Engage the shop-floor people— explain why there is a need to change.

- Be specific about the needs of each product family.

- Encourage open communication from workers.

- Alleviate the possessiveness of department supervisors—explain the theory of participative management.

- Clearly explain the metrics that will be used during the kaizen event, and how they are different than standard costing metrics.

- Get the okay to get rid of distractions during the event.

Areas for the Next Four Events

Team Two identified the following four areas.

- Stamping and forging—This area is a key bottleneck. Holding an event here will have the most positive impact on overall production. Quality is poor with excessive scrap, impacting the rest of the plant. There is the possibility new equipment will be needed.

- Heavy machining—Possessing the nucleus of a great area for successful kaizen, several employees have already had extensive exposure to the Toyota Production System (TPS). Heavy machining was chosen as the best place to develop future leaders and showcase kaizen events.

- Grinding—Part movement in this area is poor. Dramatic improvement could be made by consolidating the operation. There is a potential for substantial labor savings by having operators run multiple machines.

- Welding—The welding team is loaded with technical people and if they are enthusiastic, much could be accomplished. The department's numbers are not very good.

Assumptions

Team Two made the following assumptions.

- Overtime or the transfer of workers from other areas will cover team members' regular jobs during the event.

- Displaced workers will be redeployed elsewhere in the plant. No layoffs will result from the improvements.

- The replacement parts area needs to improve lead time. It is currently the worst area.

- There are four major product lines: 1) replacement parts; 2) electric-powered hand tools; 3) small hand tools; and 4) original equipment manufacturer (OEM) tools.

Team Member Selection and Why

Stamping and Forging Team

The stamping and forging team consists of seven members, including the team leader. Here are the people who were chosen.

Team leader, Carol Butts— Carol is the production supervisor in the area. He has good technical experience and wants improvements made.

Co-leader, Adrian Swift—As a supplier, he has had extensive exposure to kaizen at his company. Adrian also has been a co-leader before. He has working knowledge of steel and stamping operations, and is respected by DEMCO management.

Brenda Stabil—As production manager, she has seen a lot of the plant in her 22 years. Brenda has a good idea of how product flows. She was on the first kaizen event team and was skeptical at first. Brenda has ideas on how to improve the next event.

Miles Standish—Working in the heavy machining department, he is familiar with TPS. Miles has a good mix of tradesmen in his department who are also familiar with kaizen and TPS. He is currently in training for a later event in his department.

Robert Cook—As tool room supervisor, he has great technical experience and can assist in getting things made quickly if needed. Robert is also experienced at repairing the tools and dies used in the stamping and forging operations.

In addition, two operators from the stamping area, one from each shift, will join the team.

Heavy Machining Team

The heavy machining team also consists of seven members, including the team leader. Here are the people who were chosen.

Team leader, Miles Standish—He was on a previous event in the stamping and forging area. He is supervisor of the heavy machining department and should be able to get right into the thick of the problems and expedite improvements. Miles has been planning for the past three weeks for this event.

Co-leader, Harold Stassen—As a sales engineer with a machine builder/supplier, he knows all about the machines in the department. His company sold most of them to DEMCO. Harold has been to Japan several times and has seen kaizen events there. He also has been on those at his company. Harold is respected by DEMCO management.

Eduardo Polaski—As director of engineering and a core team member, he will be instrumental in defining the kaizen direction. Eduardo has knowledge of companies that are considered "benchmarks." He can take the kaizen philosophy back to engineering to make improvements there since many of the machining area's problems stem from engineering-related issues. Eduardo will continue to be involved in subsequent events.

Hayden Proffitt—As material handling supervisor, he can provide forklift assistance if and when needed. Hayden will be asked to assist in future machinery moves. He was quite busy with the last event and attended the report-out.

In addition, one die maker from the stamping and forging area will join the team. He has a good technical background and training, and can operate all the machines in the department. He did some work for the last event and attended the report-out. Two operators from the area, one from each shift will also join the team. Both are volunteers and have had preliminary training delivered by human resources. They welcome change for the better.

Grinding Team

The grinding team consists of six members, including the team leader. Here are the people who were chosen.

Team leader, Robert Cook— Robert participated in the first kaizen event in the stamping and forging area. He is also familiar with SMED and TPS. As supervisor of the tool room, he has good analytical abilities and has run most of the machines in the grinding area.

Co-leader, Robert Nowak— As supervisor of the grinding area, he has working knowledge of all the processes. Robert would like to consolidate all the machines into one area, as he currently has to chase from one end of the plant to the other. He thinks he can keep an eye

on things better if he can be around all of the operators more.

Billy Bob Thornton—As welding department supervisor, he is in training for a later event to be held in his area. If Billy Bob can grasp the kaizen concept he may stay on to implement it in his area. But if he feels that he is in over his head, Billy Bob plans to retire.

In addition, two operators from the area, one from each shift, will join the team. One is the setup operator from the far side of the plant on second shift. A forklift operator from third shift will also come aboard. He moved many machines during the last event but he was not a team member. To cover his regular duties, he will be replaced by the day-shift driver coming in four hours early and the second-shift driver staying four hours overtime.

Welding Team

The welding team consists of seven members, including the team leader. Here are the people who were chosen.

Team leader, Billy Bob Thornton—He was on the last kaizen team in the grinding area.

As supervisor of the welding area, it is up to him to implement kaizen here.

Co-leader, Peter Paytol— Manager of shipping/receiving, one of his drivers is also on the team. Peter was on the first kaizen event and asked to be on another one.

Miles Standish—As supervisor of the heavy machining area, he was team leader on the kaizen event held there. So, he knows first-hand what has to be done to implement change in an area after it has been "kaizened." Miles is one of the most knowledgeable supervisors when it comes to understanding how kaizen works.

In addition, an operator from the area on first shift and a welding technician who does setups and minor adjustments to the welding equipment will join the team. The welding technician had formal welding training in the Army. A maintenance man who works in the area to support production will also participate. He has been to welder repair school and is interested in making improvements to the area as he thinks the machines break down too much. A forklift operator from Peter Paytol's area will also serve on the team. He moved some machines at the second event.

Conclusion and Critique

The final assessment of Team Two's exercise follows.

- The key lessons learned were good observations and correct.

- The changes Team Two would make are sound.

- The areas chosen for the next events are indicative of the team thinking that major changes need to be made to the core processes. For the learning value, the team chose to tackle areas in the plant that have excellent potential for success due to the personnel in those areas.

- There is good diversity to their plan: attack the operational problems first, and then look to the benefits of training after the first two events.

- Cost could be a limiting factor in what can be accomplished during the event if success is based on new machines improving the department.

- Because of the many technical elements in stamping and heavy machining, serious thought should be given to the goals and objectives of the event. Are they realistic? In comparison, chances for success in the grinding and welding areas will be a lot better.

- Beginning with the two most difficult areas in regard to machinery and monuments can result in most of the tasks ending up on the follow-up sheet. Little actually gets changed or improved during the event.

- The third and fourth events could have been combined to allow two weeks to achieve the expected results.

Exercise grade is 81%—a "B." Team Two's first two events will have limited success and need more than normal follow-up. The third and fourth will have a better chance of success and will be more obvious to the rest of the organization.

Team Three

Team Three chose to hold its first event in the area with the most WIP and backorders, thus realizing immediate dollar savings from improvements. The team members chose the areas from a matrix they developed. The matrix helped to determine which areas would give the largest

immediate impact. Team Three plans to fund the remaining three events through the savings realized from the first event.

Key Lessons Learned

The lessons observed by Team Three are outlined as follows.

- There must be long-range preparation and a daily event schedule.

- TPS training is needed.

- Appropriate data must be available.

- Operators must be included on the team and the report-out should include all team members.

- Production is needed on the kaizen lines during the event to test improvements.

- There must be a celebration.

- There should be mandatory follow-up with all staff.

- There should be coordination and communication with the unions.

- The team needs a strong leader with previous experience who is not biased.

- It should be communicated that managers are to act as participants, not leaders.

- The core team was not trained well enough to plan the first event.

- Enthusiasm was missing.

What Could be Done Differently

Team Three came up with the following list of things that could be done differently.

- Pick an area sure to meet with immediate success and a positive financial return.

- Define the scope and objectives clearly.

- Pick the team and start preparation work (training) as soon as possible.

- Conduct weekly team member meetings to review check sheets.

- Develop a list of supplies needed and have them on-hand for the event.

- Plan the week's schedule and agenda, and publish it before the event.

- Make preliminary maintenance arrangements.

- Communicate to the shop-floor people the need to change.

- Encourage open communication from workers.

- Alleviate the possessiveness of department supervisors. Explain the theory of participative management.

- Clearly explain the metrics that will be used during the kaizen event and how they differ from standard costing metrics.

- Get the okay to run production processes during the event.

Areas for the Next Four Events

Team Three chose to tackle those processes with the most potential for success and that collectively represent a large portion of production—53%.

- Stamping and forging—This area is a key bottleneck. Holding an event here will address the area with the most impact on overall production. Quality is poor with excessive scrap, which impacts the rest of the plant. The area will need new equipment.

- Low-volume special equipment—This area has the lowest scrap rate, but has the most unstable production schedule. The department has the highest cost of operation and is least efficient. The whole department may be eliminated since its main purpose is to expedite rush orders.

- Small hand tools—With the second highest numbers for WIP, high back-order quantities, and high scrap rate, this area represents the largest percentage of business volume (22%). The area's workers are ambitious. This elephant may take too long to digest!

- OEE tools—This area has the second highest number of back-orders, fairly high WIP, and fair quality.

Assumptions

In choosing the kaizen areas, Team Three made the following assumptions.

- During the event, the regular jobs of team members will be covered by overtime or transfers of workers from other areas.

- Displaced workers will be redeployed elsewhere in the plant. No layoffs will occur as a result of improvements.

- The replacement parts area needs to improve lead time. It is currently the worst area.

- There are four major product lines: 1) replacement parts; 2) electric-powered hand tools; 3) small hand tools; and 4) OEM tools.

Team Member Selection and Why

Stamping and Forging Team

The stamping and forging team consists of nine members, including the team leader. Here are the people who were chosen.

Team leader, Dinty Moore— He is the lean champion and wants to see this area improve.

Co-leader, Carol Butts—Carol is the production supervisor in the area. He has good technical experience and wants changes made.

Adrian Swift—As a supplier to DEMCO, he has had extensive exposure to kaizen at his company. Adrian has been a co-leader before. He has working knowledge of steel and stamping, and is respected by DEMCO management.

Eduardo Polaski—As director of engineering, he will be instrumental in defining kaizen direction. He is a core team member. Eduardo has knowledge of companies considered to be "benchmarks." He can take the kaizen philosophy back to engineering to make improvements since many of the machining area's problems stem from engineering-related issues.

Reginald Oxwald—As chief buyer for SFX Company, he has been to a public kaizen event. He is not familiar with DEMCO's processes, which will allow him to look at things with a fresh set of eyes.

Roger Summers—As manager of maintenance and a journeyman electrician, he knows a lot about the machines in the area. Roger was on the first event, but had to leave many times to put out fires. He will help get things done.

In addition, the union steward from the stamping and forging area will join the team. He is familiar with the way kaizen works. Adding creditability, he will ensure that workers know the union is in favor of these events. And, two operators from the stamping area, one from each shift, will participate on the team.

Low-volume Special Equipment Team

The low-volume special equipment team consists of eight members, including the team leader. Here are the people who were chosen.

Team leader, Carol Butts—Carol is the production supervisor in the stamping area. He has good technical experience and wants changes made. Carol was on the last kaizen team as co-leader.

Co-leader, Adrian Swift—A supplier to DEMCO, he has had extensive exposure to kaizen with his company. Adrian has been a co-leader before. He has working knowledge of steel and stamping and is respected by DEMCO management.

Karen Johnson—Director of human resources, she has experience as a trainer and knows about TPS.

Eduardo Polaski—As director of engineering, he will be instrumental in defining kaizen direction. Eduardo is a core team member and has knowledge of companies that are considered "benchmarks." He can take the kaizen philosophy back to engineering to make improvements since many of the machining area's problems stem from engineering-related issues. Eduardo will continue to be involved with subsequent events.

Roger Summers—As manager of maintenance and a journeyman electrician, he knows about the machines in the area. He was on the first event.

Rex Norad—From the heat treating department, he knows about the product.

In addition, two operators from the low-volume, special equipment area, one from each shift, will join the team.

Small Hand Tools Team

The small hand tools team consists of eight members, including the team leader. Here are the people who were chosen.

Team leader, Adrian Swift—A DEMCO supplier, he has had extensive exposure to kaizen with his company. Adrian was a co-leader before and this will be his first time as leader. He has working knowledge of steel and stamping and is respected by DEMCO management.

Co-leader, Karen Johnson—She has experience as a trainer and knows about TPS.

In addition, three operators from the low-volume, special equipment area and small hand tools areas will join the team. One die maker from the stamping and forging area who has a good technical background and training will also participate. He has experience operating all the machines in the department. He did some work on a past event and attended the report-out.

OEM Tools Team

The OEM tools team consists of nine members, including the team leader. Here are the people who were chosen.

Team leader, Dinty Moore—He is the lean champion and wants to see this area improve.

Co-leader, Carol Butts—Carol supervises the stamping and forging lines. He has good technical experience and wants improvements made.

Adrian Swift—A DEMCO supplier, he has had extensive exposure to kaizen with his company. Adrian has been a co-leader before. He has working knowledge of steel and stamping and is respected by DEMCO management.

Eduardo Polaski—As director of engineering, he will be instrumental in defining kaizen direction. Eduardo is a core team member and has knowledge of companies considered to be "benchmarks." He can take the kaizen philosophy back to engineering to make improvements since many of the machining area's problems stem from engineering-related issues.

Rex Norad—From the heat treating department, he knows about the product.

Roger Summers—As manager of maintenance and a journeyman electrician, he knows about the machines in the area. He was on the first event and will help get things done.

In addition, the union steward from the stamping and forging area will join the team. He is familiar with the way kaizen works. Adding credibility, he will ensure that workers know the union is in favor of these events. And, two operators from the stamping area, one from each shift, will participate on the team.

Conclusion and Critique

The final assessment for Team Three is as follows.

- The key lessons learned were good and correct.

- The changes that Team Three would make are sound.

- The areas chosen for the next events are in keeping with the team's recognition of the need for major changes to the core processes. For learning value, Team Three chose to tackle areas that have excellent potential to succeed.

- There is good diversity to Team Three's plan: attack the operational problems first, and then look to the monetary and customer satisfaction benefits.

- Cost could be a limiting factor for what can be accomplished during the first event if success is based on new machines improving the department.

- Because there are many technical elements in stamping, serious thought should be given to the goals and objectives of that event. Are they realistic?

- Success in the low-volume special equipment area will be seen differently since it already has the best scrap rate and lower volume and inventories.

- The third and fourth events, small hand tools and OEM tools, address areas that represent one third of the production requirements, and well over $560,000 in back-orders. Reducing WIP from currently over $580,000 and reducing back-orders will help improve cash flow quickly.

- A more comprehensive matrix was used to make comparisons and is shown in Table C-4.

- Team member selections tie-in with experience, training, and future needs.

Exercise grade is 86%—a "B." The first two events will be difficult and need more than normal follow-up. The third and fourth will have better chances of success—freeing up cash and pleasing customers.

Team Four

Team Four chose its first event by using a matrix the team developed. The team wanted to target an area that would have the largest impact on the revenue stream. The four areas chosen collectively generate over 63% of DEMCO's revenue. Two of the areas, electronic specialty tools (18%) and re-placement parts (24%), represent 42%. These areas also have substantial back-order value—over $1 million. The kaizen events held in these areas can add quick dollars to cash flow.

Key Lessons Learned

Team Four has noted the following observations.

- A kaizen event coordinator should be appointed.

- Management commitment and physical presence should be obvious.

- There must be a celebration.

- Appropriate data must be available.

- Production is needed on the kaizen lines during the event to test improvements.

- There should be mandatory follow-up with all staff.

- There should be coordination and communication with the unions.

- There should be a report-out that utilizes all team members.

- The importance of the event should be made known to everyone.

Team Exercise: Deluxe Elaborate Manufacturing Company (DEMCO)

Table C-4. Kaizen Event Area Selection Matrix

#	Product Line	Priority	Business Volume	Revenue	Scrap Rate	Work in process/ Inventory	Back-orders	Manufacturing Lead Time	Number of Processes
1	Small hand tools		22%	9%	6.0%	$356,000	$267,000	34 days	9
2	Medium hand tools		13%	11%	5.0%	$187,000	$237,000	29 days	9
3	Large hand tools		4%	2%	4.0%	$235,000	$199,800	41 days	12
4	Electric-powered hand tools		12%	13%	6.5%	$287,800	$202,000	40 days	11
5	Electric-powered special tools		3%	3%	7.0%	$167,900	$ 34,500	28 days	10
6	Electronic specialty tools		10%	18%	2.0%	$ 34,600	$16,800	62 days	6
7	OEM tools		12%	5%	2.3%	$238,900	$302,900	44 days	9
8	Export and licensee tooling		5%	7%	1.0%	$239,900	$190,000	48 days	7
9	Low-volume special equipment		2%	3%	0.3%	$ 66,300	$43,200	70 days	9
10	Replacement parts		17%	24%	4.6%	$1,700,000	$553,000	22 days	7

- Supplies should be on-hand and arrangements should be made for maintenance help.

What Could be Done Differently

Team Four observed the following things that could be done differently.

- Define the scope and objectives and clearly establish ground rules.

- Pick the team and start preparation work and training as soon as possible.

- Stress the importance of the kaizen event. It is the most important thing happening that week.

- Develop a list of supplies needed and have them on-hand for the event.

- Plan the week's schedule and agenda, and publish it before the event.

- Make preliminary maintenance arrangements.

- Communicate with the shop-floor workers about why there is the need to change.

- Select a coordinator who has good organizational skills.

- Alleviate the possessiveness of department supervisors. Explain the theory of participative management.

- Clearly explain the metrics that will be used during the kaizen event and how they differ from standard costing metrics.

- Get the okay to run production processes during the event.

Areas for the Next Four Events

Team Four has chosen the following areas.

- Replacement parts—This area represents the largest percentage of revenue—24%. A kaizen event here will have the most impact on cash flow and customer satisfaction. The area has the largest WIP, $1,700,000, and back-orders of $553,000.

- Small hand tools—The area has the highest volume of business—22%. It also has the second highest WIP—$356,000. An event here would support Team Four's goal of addressing high-volume areas and improving cash flow by reducing WIP and back-orders. As a result, customer satisfaction will also improve.

- Electronic specialty tools—This is the most profitable department in the company, but is plagued by slow deliveries and reliance on other departments. The area needs to stand alone and generate profits faster. This is the most promising department for growth in all of DEMCO. It can be made even more profitable.

- Electric-powered hand tools—This area has high WIP—$287,800, and back-orders of $202,000. It represents the core of the business. Improvements made here can help satisfy many customers.

Assumptions

Team Four has made the following assumptions.

- Overtime or transfers of workers from other areas will cover the team members' regular jobs during the event.

- Displaced workers will be redeployed elsewhere in the plant. No layoffs will occur as a result of improvements.

- The areas chosen have the best potential to improve cash flow.

- There are four major product lines: 1) replacement parts; 2) electric-powered hand tools; 3) small hand tools; and 4) OEM tools.

Team Member Selection and Why

Replacement Parts Team

The replacement parts team consists of nine members, including the team leader. Here are the people who were chosen.

Team leader, Eduardo Polaski—As director of engineering, he will be instrumental in defining kaizen direction. Eduardo is a core team member and has knowledge of companies that are considered to be "benchmarks." He can take the kaizen philosophy back to engineering to make improvements since many problems stem from engineering-related issues.

Co-leader, Dinty Moore—He is the lean champion and wants to see this area improve.

Rex Norad—From the heat treating department, he is familiar with the product.

Miles Standish—A supervisor in the heavy machining area, he was team leader on the first event there, so he knows first-hand what has to be done to implement change in an area after it has been "kaizened." He is one of the most knowledgeable supervisors when it comes to understanding how kaizen works.

Robert Nowak—A supervisor in the grinding area, he has good knowledge of all the parts produced.

Roger Summers—As manager of maintenance and a journeyman electrician, he knows about the machines in the area. He was on the first event and will help get things done.

Warren Wilson—As controller, his understanding of the area may be influential in getting funding for new equipment.

In addition, two operators from the area, one from each shift will join the team.

Small Hand Tools Team

The small hand tools team consists of nine members, including the team leader. Here are the people who were chosen.

Team leader, Eduardo Polaski —As director of engineering, he will be instrumental in defining kaizen direction. Eduardo is a core team member and has knowledge of companies considered to be "benchmarks." He can take the kaizen philosophy back to engineering to make improvements, since many of the machining area's problems stem from engineering-related issues.

Co-team leader, Dinty Moore —He is the lean champion and wants to see this area improve.

Rex Norad—From the heat treating department, he is familiar with the product.

Robert Nowak—As supervisor of the grinding area, he has good knowledge of all the processes.

Miles Standish— As supervisor of the heavy machining area, he was team leader on the kaizen event held there. So, he knows first-hand what has to be done to implement change to an area after it has been "kaizened." Miles is one of the most knowledgeable supervisors when it comes to understanding how kaizen works.

In addition, one maintenance person who works in the area to support production and three operators from the area, one from each shift, will join the team.

Electronic Specialty Tools Team

The electronic specialty tools team consists of eight members, including the team leader. Here are the people who were chosen.

Team leader, Eduardo Polaski —As director of engineering, he will be instrumental in defining kaizen direction. Eduardo is a core team member and has knowledge of companies considered to be "benchmarks." He can take the kaizen philosophy back to engineering to make improvements since many of the machining area's problems stem from engineering-related issues.

Co-leader, Carol Butts—He is the production supervisor in the stamping area. Carol has good technical experience and wants changes made.

Rex Norad—From the heat treating department, he is familiar with the product.

Ronald Kromm—As paint room supervisor, he is familiar with finishing electronic specialty tools.

Gerald Bixby—He is being asked on the condition that he will restrain himself from acting as the operations manager while on the event. If Gerald refuses, a replacement will be found.

In addition, one maintenance man who works in the area to support production and two operators from the electronics assembly area, one from each shift, will join the team.

Electric-powered Hand Tools Team

The electric-powered hand tools team consists of eight members, including the team leader. Here are the people who were chosen.

Team leader, Rex Norad— From the heat treating department, he is familiar with the product. Rex also has experience from being on previous teams.

Co-team leader, Eduardo Polaski—As director of engineering, he will be instrumental in defining kaizen direction. Eduardo is a core team member and has knowledge of companies considered to be "benchmarks." He can take the kaizen philosophy back to engineering to make improvements since many of the machining area's problems stem from engineering-related issues. Eduardo also has past experience as a team leader.

Gerald Bixby—He is being asked on the condition that he will restrain himself from acting as the operations manager while on the event. If Gerald refuses, a replacement will be found.

Also joining the team is a tool-and-die maker from the tool room, because he knows more about the details of the process than anyone and he can get new tools and parts made quickly. And, a union steward from the stamping and forging area will also participate. Adding credibility to the cause, he is familiar with kaizen and will ensure that workers know the union is in favor of these events. Three operators from the area, one from each shift, will also join the team.

Conclusion and Critique

The final assessment of Team Four is as follows.

- The key lessons learned were good observations and correct.

- The changes that Team Four would make are for differing reasons than the previous teams. They are reasonable and sound and show a unique flair.

- The areas chosen for the next events are indicative of the

team thinking that there are some great opportunities to improve cash flow and profitability, as well as grow the company.

- There is good diversity to Team Four's plan: attack the operational problems in areas generating the major portions of revenue first; then look to customer satisfaction benefits.

- The team used two matrices, one showing the normal comparisons and the second the profit ratios base. Team members looked at the total dollars involved to get the "biggest bang for the buck."

- Improvements in the replacement parts area will be visually and financially rewarding since the area has the most WIP. It will take some time to bleed off the inventory, so the area will not appear much different right after the event. This area represents another "elephant," which can not be completely addressed in one event over just a few days.

- The second event addresses an area representing the largest segment of the business, small hand tools. This area has high

WIP—$356,000 and high back-orders—$267,000. Improvements to this area will greatly improve cash flow. A way must be found to build the correct parts. High WIP and back-orders indicate that the wrong parts are being built. The event must solve this dilemma.

- The third event is to be in the Park Drive facility that makes electronic specialty tools. This area has the highest profit margin and the highest potential for increased profits. It needs to cut loose from its dependence on the other areas and services so it can reorganize and consolidate operations to make some much needed space.

- The last event will be in the electric-powered hand tools area. The area has high WIP—$287,800 and back-orders of $202,000. Representing the company's core business, improvements made here will satisfy many customers.

- The other areas are somewhat "elephants" in their own right, but have the best possibilities for financial success when completed.

Exercise grade is 92%—an "A." The four areas represent 64% of DEMCO's revenue, 61% of the volume, and $2,378,400 in WIP or 68%. Although these numbers are large, there are two unique situations:

- The Park Drive facility would benefit tremendously if it were a separate company. It could grow and be more profitable, and reduce manufacturing lead time, generating cash even faster. It already has the best profit margin.

- Park Drive could be the ideal "pilot line" where a showcase operation is developed. It could become a wholly, self-contained manufacturing company within DEMCO. As a learning tool, it could be the best kaizen in the plant.

TEAM EXERCISE CONCLUSION

For lean to be sustainable at DEMCO, there needs to be total commitment from top management. Before further kaizen events are held, management must agree on the following:

- The entire organization will become "lean."

- The importance of lean and commitment to the philosophy will be communicated to everyone, at all levels.

- Everybody will be asked for their commitment and "buy-in" because changes will affect everyone.

- Lean is not another "flavor of the month."

- Management will lead by being leaders, not managers.

- Change will be 80% cultural and 20% physical.

- Old paradigms will be cast aside in favor of participative management.

- Old metrics will not be used to measure lean progress. New metrics must be adopted.

- There will be no turning back. And, there can be no reluctant participants, at any level. There is no room for "cement heads."

- Sufficient resources, including personnel and capital, must be made available.

- To prevent regression, constant attention must be paid to the progress of the teams and overall state of the business.

- The lean journey may be the most important endeavor to ever take place within the company. It is the future.

Once management has agreed, then the individual plants and operations must take the following steps:

- The importance of kaizen events will be communicated to everyone at all levels.

- Everybody in the company will be asked for their commitment because the changes will affect everyone.

- Embrace that lean is not another "flavor of the month."

- Old metrics will not be used to measure lean progress. New metrics will be adopted.

- It will be communicated to all that freed-up operators will not be laid-off. They will be redeployed elsewhere.

- Management will lead by being leaders, not managers.

- Implement change that will be 80% cultural and 20% physical.

- Old paradigms will be cast aside in favor of participative management.

- It will be communicated that there is no room for "cement heads." There can be no reluctant participants, at any level.

- Each plant must have a lean champion and staff assigned to the core team.

- When an event is held, the decisions and conclusions are binding. The plant manager cannot arbitrarily veto or change the event plan, except with the concurrence of the team responsible for the improvements.

Appendix D

Team Leader Checklists

This appendix contains the same team leader checklists presented in Chapter 7, but in reproducible size. Readers are permitted to duplicate these as needed.

Product Routing Checklist

❏ Review layout with team.

❏ Go to plant, walk the part flow.

❏ Locate each machine by number.

❏ Transfer data to the Standard Work Sheet.

❏ Get data for and perform the Product Quantity Analysis.

❏ From above information, group products by common processes and operations, and then in descending order by volume.

❏ Complete the equipment and Process Routing Matrix. The matrix groups the products or parts according to the processes they require for completion.

❏ Select a product by Pareto analysis.

Current Process Mapping Checklist

❏ Complete the Standard Work Sheet.

❏ Route products and measure travel distance.

❏ Calculate square footage occupied by the current process.

❏ Count all work in process (WIP).

❏ Count current staffing.

❏ Determine all support persons assigned to the area.

❏ Investigate changeovers and their frequency.

❏ Investigate the current scrap rate and where it comes from.

❏ Determine bottlenecks and their reason.

Time-data Collection Checklist

❏ Talk to the operators prior to doing time studies. Discuss the intent of the kaizen on their line.

❏ Time study each operator and record results on the Time Observation Sheet.

❏ Calculate the takt time.

❏ Complete the Process Design Analysis Sheet.

❏ Calculate the theoretical lead time.

❏ Document any unique processes or handling required.

❏ Determine the changeover frequency and times.

❏ Construct a spaghetti diagram.

Future State Mapping Checklist

❑ Ask, "What would this process be if it were waste-free?"

❑ Review the 10 forms of muda (waste). Is there any here?

❑ Brainstorm—use a board to write down all ideas and then categorize them.

❑ Using the Flow Layout Sheet from the current state mapping, cut and paste a new proposed layout.

❑ Look at the details of the rearrangement, what obstacles are there?

❑ Select the best-choice alternative and develop a new layout.

❑ Complete the Process Design Analysis Sheet for the new process.

❑ Meet with the operators to collaborate on new ideas.

New Process Requirements Checklist

❏ Clean the area of focus, leaving only the essentials needed to perform the "new" tasks. Mark the floor.

❏ Make a detailed layout with instructions for maintenance personnel so they can make the moves during the night.

❏ Rearrange the process to include the work in process (WIP) needed, as well as support functions required for changeovers and tools.

❏ Continue to brainstorm with the team. Ask the operators for their input and critique of the new process.

❏ Think outside of the box—be daring!

New Process Verification Checklist

❏ Talk to the operators. Test out the new process.

❏ Observe new cycle times and note any problems.

❏ Check for any possible safety issues.

❏ Is there enough work in process (WIP) at the proper locations?

❏ Complete the Standard Work Combination Sheet.

❏ Redo the Time Observation Sheet.

❏ Itemize all implemented improvements. Determine the costs of implementation.

❏ Calculate all savings—including part travel, operator travel, throughput time, operator savings, square footage, etc.

Report-out Preparation Checklist

❏ All operators are trained on the new process.

❏ The process is actually running and producing good parts at the cycle times established.

❏ Hard copies of the presentation are complete with overheads.

❏ Review Process Design Analysis Sheet.

❏ All Standard Work Sheets are complete with takt times.

❏ Safety improvements are made (three per day or one per team member).

❏ List possible future improvements.

❏ All analysis work is complete with comparisons of old and new process plotted on charts.

❏ New layout is complete.

❏ Costs/benefits calculations are figured and documented.

❏ Follow-up ("30-day") list is compiled.

❏ All necessary documentation (ISO 9000) is complete.

Index